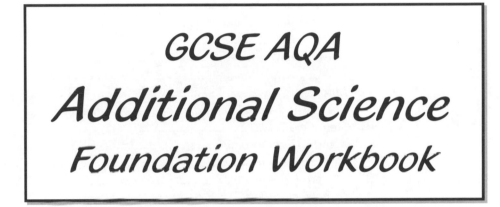

GCSE AQA
Additional Science
Foundation Workbook

This book is for anyone doing **GCSE AQA Additional Science** at foundation level. It covers everything you'll need for your year 11 exams.

It's full of **tricky questions**... each one designed to make you **sweat** — because that's the only way you'll get any **better**.

There are questions to see **what facts** you know. There are questions to see how well you can **apply those facts**. And there are questions to see what you know about **how science works**.

It's also got some daft bits in to try and make the whole experience at least vaguely entertaining for you.

What CGP is all about

Our sole aim here at CGP is to produce the highest quality books — carefully written, immaculately presented and dangerously close to being funny.

Then we work our socks off to get them out to you — at the cheapest possible prices.

Contents

Published by CGP

Editors: Charlotte Burrows, Katherine Craig, Emma Elder, Mary Falkner, Felicity Inkpen, Jane Sawers, Camilla Simson, Dawn Wright.

Contributors: Mike Dagless, Max Fishel, Dr Giles R Greenway, Dr Iona MJ Hamilton, Rebecca Harvey, Frederick Langridge, Sidney Stringer Community School.

ISBN: 978 1 84762 760 5

With thanks to Chris Elliss, Ben Fletcher, Ian Francis, Julie Jackson, Hayley Thompson and Jane Towle for the proofreading.

With thanks to Laura Jakubowski for the copyright research.

Every effort has been made to locate copyright holders and obtain permission to reproduce sources. For those sources where it has been difficult to trace the originator of the work, we would be grateful for information. If any copyright holder would like us to make an amendment to the acknowledgements, please notify us and we will gladly update the book at the next reprint. Thank you.

Pages 123 and 125 contain public sector information published by the Health and Safety Executive and licensed under the Open Government Licence v1.0.

www.cgpbooks.co.uk

Printed by Elanders Ltd, Newcastle upon Tyne.
Clipart from Corel®
Based on the classic CGP style created by Richard Parsons.

Cells

Q1 Plant and animal cells have **similarities** and **differences**.
Complete each statement below by choosing the correct words.

a) Only **plant** / animal cells contain chloroplasts.

b) Plant cells have a **vacuole** / **cell wall**, which is made of cellulose.

c) Plant and animal cells contain ribosomes, which are where **fats** / **proteins** are made in the cell.

d) The cell **wall** / **membrane** holds the cell together and controls what goes in and out.

Q2 Below are three structures found in plant cells. Draw lines to match each structure to its function.

Nucleus — absorbs light energy to make food for the plant

Chloroplast — contains DNA that controls the activities of the cell

Cell wall — strengthens the cell

Q3 **Mitochondria** are very important cell structures.

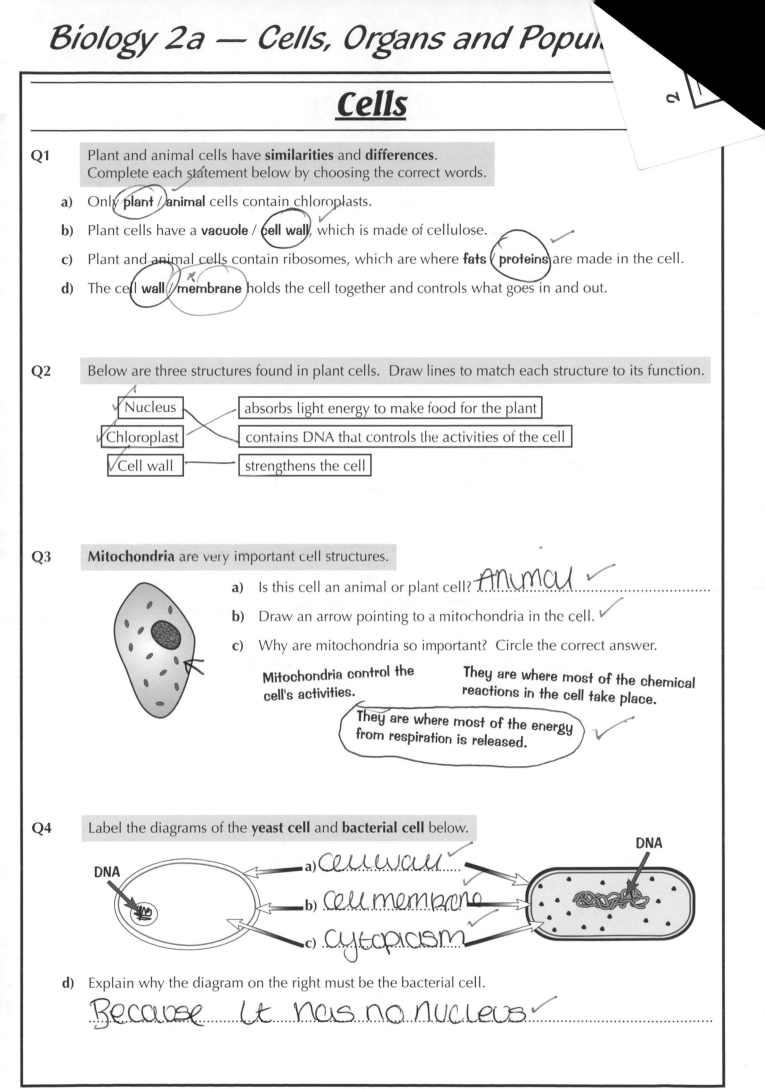

a) Is this cell an animal or plant cell? Animal

b) Draw an arrow pointing to a mitochondria in the cell.

c) Why are mitochondria so important? Circle the correct answer.

Mitochondria control the cell's activities.

They are where most of the chemical reactions in the cell take place.

They are where most of the energy from respiration is released.

Q4 Label the diagrams of the **yeast cell** and **bacterial cell** below.

DNA

DNA

a) Cell wall

b) Cell membrane

c) Cytoplasm

d) Explain why the diagram on the right must be the bacterial cell.

Because it has no nucleus

Diffusion

Q1   Complete the passage below by choosing the most appropriate words.

Diffusion is the spreading out of particles from an area of **high** / **low** concentration

to an area of **high** / **low** concentration. Particles move both ways, but there

is a **net** / **rod** movement of particles from the area of high concentration.

The bigger the difference in concentration, the **faster** / **slower** the rate of diffusion.

Q2   The diagram on the left shows a **cup of water** which has just had a small **drop of dye** added.

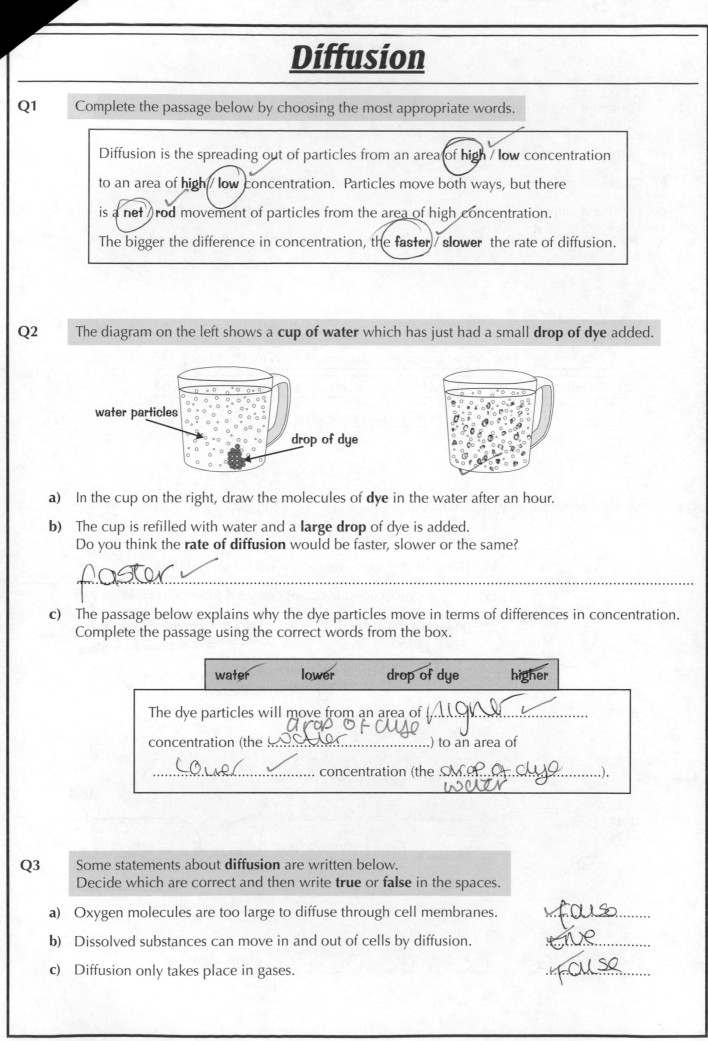

water particles

drop of dye

a)   In the cup on the right, draw the molecules of **dye** in the water after an hour.

b)   The cup is refilled with water and a **large drop** of dye is added.
Do you think the **rate of diffusion** would be faster, slower or the same?

faster ✓

c)   The passage below explains why the dye particles move in terms of differences in concentration.
Complete the passage using the correct words from the box.

water	lower	drop of dye	higher

The dye particles will move from an area of ....higher..... ✓ ....

concentration (the ....water....... *drop of dye*.) to an area of

.........lower........ ✓ .... concentration (the ...drop of dye.........).
                                                    water

Q3   Some statements about **diffusion** are written below.
Decide which are correct and then write **true** or **false** in the spaces.

a)   Oxygen molecules are too large to diffuse through cell membranes.   false

b)   Dissolved substances can move in and out of cells by diffusion.   true

c)   Diffusion only takes place in gases.   false

Diffusion

Q4   Two models of diffusion are shown below.

A   cell membrane   **B**

a)   Would you expect the molecules to diffuse **faster** in situation A or B? ....B....

b)   Explain your answer.

Because theyies less molecues to diffuse ✓

Q5   Phil placed equal amounts of glucose solution and starch solution inside a bag. He then put the bag into a beaker of water. The bag acted like a cell membrane.

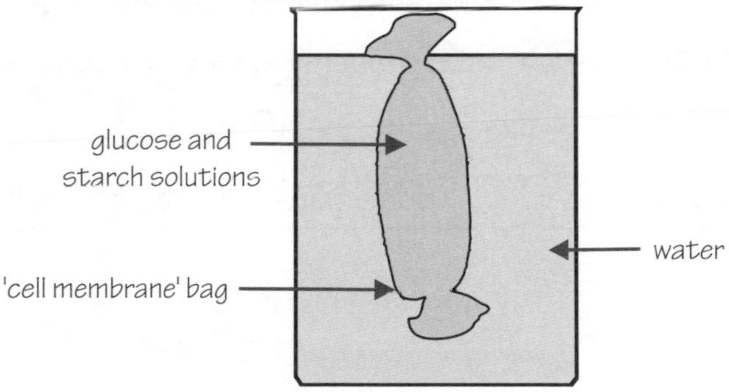

glucose and
starch solutions

'cell membrane' bag

water

After 20 minutes, Phil tested the water outside the bag to see if there was any starch or glucose in it. He found only glucose in the water.

a)   Why was there no starch in the water outside the bag?

Because the cell membrane bag kept it all in + starch too large to fit through the pores molecules are in the membrane.

Have a think about the size of the molecules — it'll help you answer this question.

b)   How did the glucose get into the water outside the bag?

because it dissolved in the bag and diffused into the water ✓

Top Tips: Don't forget it's only small molecules that can diffuse through cell membranes — amino acids, for example. Things like proteins are just too darn big to fit through.

Specialised Cells and Tissues

Q1 Tick the boxes to show whether the following statements are **true** or **false**.

True False

a) You are a multicellular organism. ☑ ☐

b) Large multicellular organisms have different systems inside them for exchanging and transporting substances. ☑ ☐

c) Differentiation occurs once a multicellular organism has finished developing. ☑ ☑

d) Specialised cells are cells that carry out a specific function. ☑ ☐

e) Specialised cells form organs, which form tissues. ☑ ☑

Q2 Complete the following paragraph about **tissues**, using the words below.

~~contracts~~   ~~similar cells~~   ~~covers~~   ~~enzymes~~   ~~function~~

A tissue is a group of ....*similar cells*.... that work together

to carry out a particular ....*function*....

In mammals (like humans), tissues include muscular tissue, glandular tissue and epithelial tissue.

Muscular tissue ....*contracts*.... (shortens) to move whatever it's attached to.

Glandular tissue makes substances like ....*enzymes*.... and hormones.

Epithelial tissue ....*covers*.... some parts of the body, e.g. the inside of the gut.

Q3 There are lots of different types of **specialised cells**.

a) Give **one** example of a specialised cell.

guard cells palisade cells

b) What is the **function** of the specialised cell you named in part **a)**?

opens and closes the stomata
carrys at photosythesis

c) i) Give one special feature of the cell you named in part **a)**.
contains lots of chloroplasts
sensitive to light at night they close
so the plant doesn't lose out on photosynthesis

ii) How does this feature help the cell to carry out its function?
chloroplasts are needed for photosynthesis
keeps the plant full of energy

Organs and Organ Systems

Q1 Sort the following list by writing each term in the correct place in the table below.

cat   blood   digestive system

liver   excretory system   snail

reproductive system   muscle   eye

Tissue	Organ	Organ system	Organism
muscle blood	liver eye	digestive system reproductive system excretory system	cat snail

Q2 The diagram below shows how cells in the digestive system are organised. Put the words below in the correct order to fill in the boxes.

stomach

human

epithelial cells

epithelial tissue

human

St epithelial cells

stomach

digestive system

epithelial Tissue
human

Q3 Fill in the boxes to label this diagram of the **digestive system**. One has been done for you.

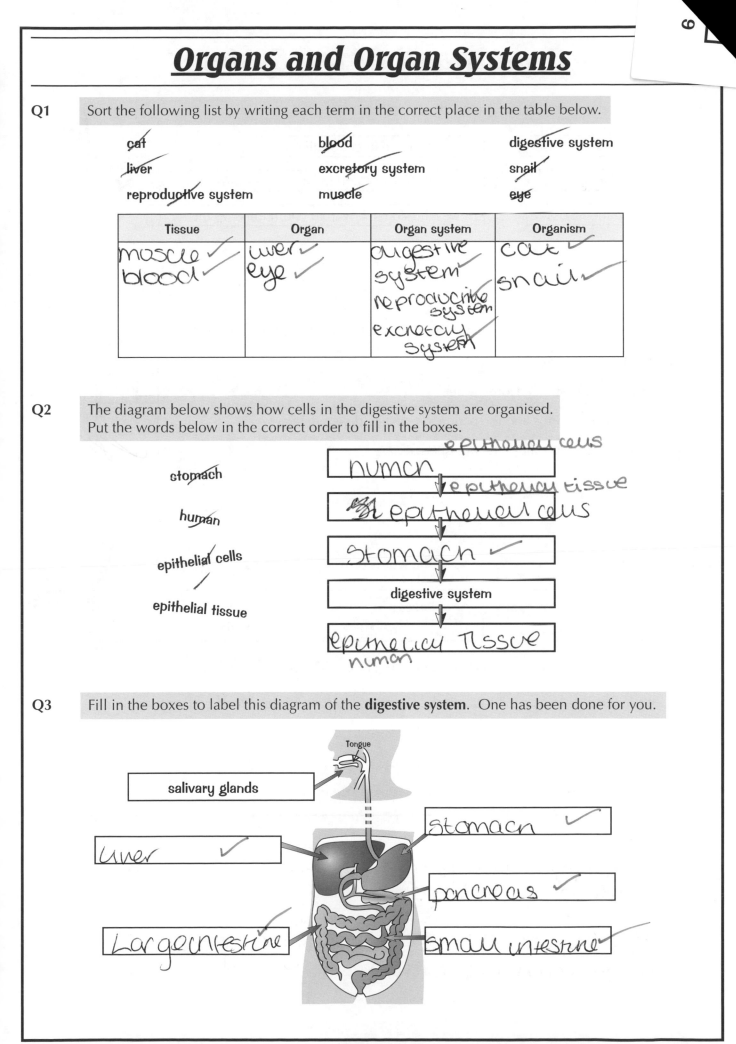

Tongue

salivary glands

stomach

liver

pancreas

Large intestine

small intestine

Biology 2a — Cells, Organs and Populations

Organs and Organ Systems

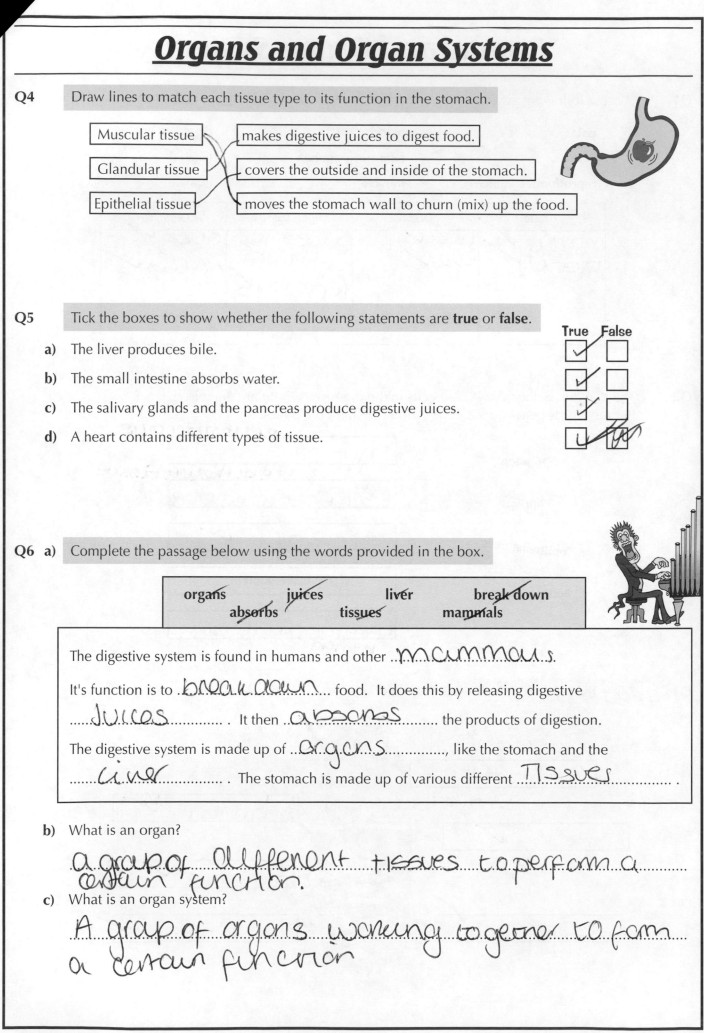

Q4 Draw lines to match each tissue type to its function in the stomach.

Muscular tissue	makes digestive juices to digest food.
Glandular tissue	covers the outside and inside of the stomach.
Epithelial tissue	moves the stomach wall to churn (mix) up the food.

Q5 Tick the boxes to show whether the following statements are **true** or **false**.

True False

a) The liver produces bile. ✓

b) The small intestine absorbs water. ✓

c) The salivary glands and the pancreas produce digestive juices. ✓

d) A heart contains different types of tissue. ✓

Q6 a) Complete the passage below using the words provided in the box.

organs   juices   liver   break down
absorbs   tissues   mammals

The digestive system is found in humans and other ..mammal..s.

It's function is to ..break down.... food. It does this by releasing digestive
.....juices........... . It then ...absorbs......... the products of digestion.

The digestive system is made up of ...organs............, like the stomach and the
.......liver............. . The stomach is made up of various different ..Tissues........... .

b) What is an organ?

a group of different tissues to perform a certain function.

c) What is an organ system?

A group of organs working together to form a certain function

Biology 2a — Cells, Organs and Populations

Plant Structure and Photosynthesis

Q1 **Photosynthesis** is the process that produces 'food' in plants.
Use the words below to complete the equation for photosynthesis.

~~oxygen~~   ~~carbon dioxide~~   ~~water~~   ~~glucose~~

carbon dioxide + *water* → (sunlight) *glucose* + *oxygen*

Q2 Plants are made up of cells, tissues, organs and organ systems.

a) Circle the right words to complete the sentences below.

i) Mesophyll tissue is where most of the **respiration /(photosynthesis in)** the plant occurs.

ii) **Muscular /(Epidermal)** tissue covers the whole plant.

iii) Xylem and phloem vessels transport substances around the **(plant) / flowers only**.

b) Name **three** organs found in a plant.

stems, leaves and roots

Q3 The rate of photosynthesis in some pondweed was recorded. This was done
by counting the bubbles produced per minute at equal intervals during the day.

No. bubbles per minute	Time of day
0	06.00
10	12.00
20	18.00
0	~~24.00~~

a) The time for the final reading is missing.
Predict what the time is likely to be.

~~12:00pm~~ *12:00pm*

Don't forget about the scales on your graph.

b) Explain why the rate of photosynthesis is
0 bubbles per minute for this time of day.

because theyres no sunlight as it's nighttime and dark

c) Plot a bar graph on the grid on the right
to display the results shown on the table.

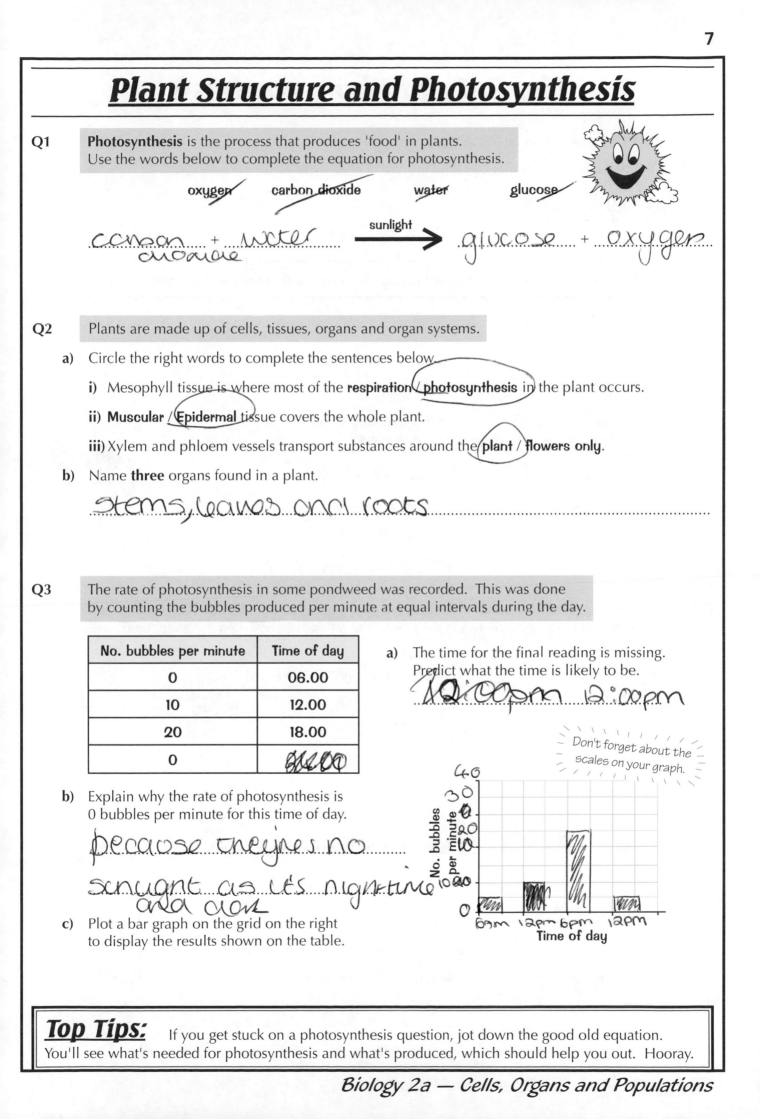

Top Tips: If you get stuck on a photosynthesis question, jot down the good old equation.
You'll see what's needed for photosynthesis and what's produced, which should help you out. Hooray.

Biology 2a — Cells, Organs and Populations

The Rate of Photosynthesis

Q1 **Light intensity** can limit the rate of photosynthesis.

a) List **two other** factors that can limit the rate of photosynthesis.

.......nightime.. winter.........................

b) Choose the correct word to complete the sentence below.

> A limiting factor is something that stops photosynthesis from going any (slower) / faster.

Q2 Farmer Fred doesn't put his cows out during the winter because the grass is not growing.

State **two** differences between summer and winter conditions
that affect the rate of photosynthesis in the grass.

1. The grass graos quicker

2. It has more nutrents

Q3 Seth investigated the effect of different concentrations of **carbon dioxide (CO$_2$)** on the rate of photosynthesis of his Swiss cheese plant. The results are shown on the graph below.

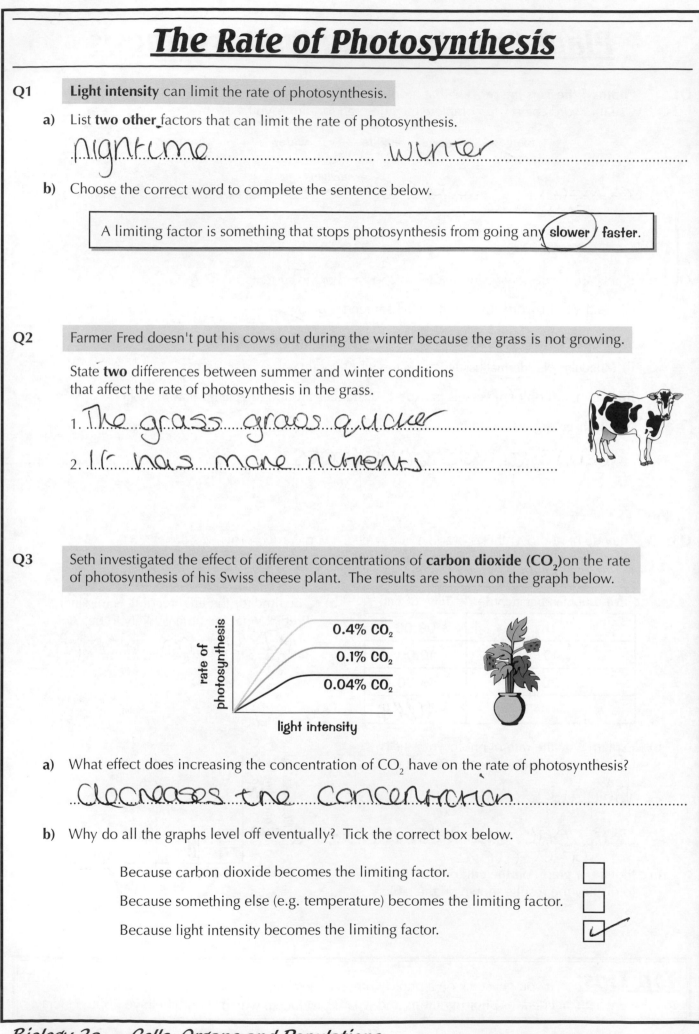

a) What effect does increasing the concentration of CO$_2$ have on the rate of photosynthesis?

....Clecreases the Concentration............................

b) Why do all the graphs level off eventually? Tick the correct box below.

Because carbon dioxide becomes the limiting factor. ☐

Because something else (e.g. temperature) becomes the limiting factor. ☐

Because light intensity becomes the limiting factor. ☑

The Rate of Photosynthesis

Q4   Lucy investigated the **volume of oxygen** (**O₂**) produced by pondweed at **different intensities of light**. Her results are shown in the table below.

Relative light intensity	1	2	3	4	5
Vol. of O₂ produced in 10 mins (ml)	12	25	13	48	61

bubbles of oxygen

pondweed

a)   What was Lucy measuring by recording the volume of oxygen produced?

The ~~volume of~~ How light intensity effects the volume of oxygen.

b)   Plot a graph of her results. One point has been plotted for you.

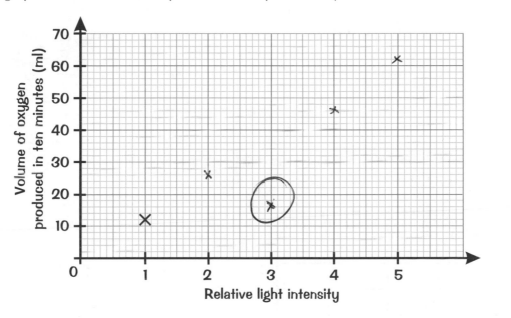

Volume of oxygen produced in ten minutes (ml)

Relative light intensity

c)   **i)**   One of Lucy's results is probably wrong. Circle this point on the graph.

  iii) Suggest what error Lucy might have made when she collected this result.

  Timed it wrong.

d)   Circle the most appropriate statement to describe the relationship shown on the graph.

  The rate of photosynthesis decreased
  as light intensity increased.

  The rate of photosynthesis increased
  as light intensity increased.

e)   What would you expect to happen to the graph if Lucy continued to increase the light intensity?

  It would ~~reach optimum~~ The volume of oxygen would increase

Biology 2a — Cells, Organs and Populations

The Rate of Photosynthesis

Q5 Graham decided to build a **greenhouse** to grow his plants in.

a) List **two** reasons why a greenhouse is an ideal environment for growing plants.

1. ....

2. ....

b) i) What could Graham add to his greenhouse in the **winter** for better growth?

....

ii) What should he use in the **summer** to ensure it doesn't get too hot?

....

iii) What could he add at **night** if he wants the plants to continue photosynthesising?

....

Q6 Average daytime summer temperatures in different habitats around the world are recorded in the table below.

Habitat	Temperature (°C)
Forest	19
Arctic	0
Desert	32
Grassland	22
Rainforest	27

a) Plot a **bar chart** for these results on the grid.

b) i) In which area would you expect the rate of photosynthesis to be **slowest**?

....

ii) Explain your answer to part **i)**.

To answer this question you'll need to think about how temperature affects enzymes.

....

....

....

How Plants Use Glucose

Q1   Complete the passage below by choosing the most appropriate words from the list.

seeds	leaves	margarine	walls	cellulose	respiration

Plants make glucose in their .... They then use some of

this glucose for .... Glucose is also made into

.... This is used to build strong cell ....

.... can store glucose in the form of fats and oils.

We can use these to make things like ....

Q2   **Plants store** some of the **glucose** for use when photosynthesis isn't happening.

a)   What do plants store glucose as?

....

b)   Is this substance **soluble** or **insoluble**?

....

c)   Name **one** place in a plant where this substance is stored.

....

Q3   Plants use glucose to make **protein**. Humans eat plants and animals as sources of protein.

a)   What ions do plants need to absorb from the soil in order to produce protein?

....

b)   Below is a graph comparing the nutrients in dhal and steak, including their protein content. What percentage of your recommended daily allowance of protein is provided by 100 g of the following?

dhal ....

steak ....

Dhal is just lentils.

c) i)   Which of these two foods provides a better source of dietary nutrients in general?

....

    ii) Explain your choice.

....

Distribution of Organisms

Q1 Tick the boxes to show whether the following statements are **true** or **false**.

<table>
<tr><td></td><td></td><td>True</td><td>False</td></tr>
<tr><td>a)</td><td>The distribution of an organism is how an organism interacts with the environment.</td><td>☐</td><td>☐</td></tr>
<tr><td>b)</td><td>You can use quadrats to study the distribution of an organism.</td><td>☐</td><td>☐</td></tr>
<tr><td>c)</td><td>The median is the smallest value when numbers are put in order of size</td><td>☐</td><td>☐</td></tr>
</table>

Q2 Environmental factors may affect where an organism is found. Which of the following are examples of environmental factors? Circle **four** answers.

how much helium there is   how much carbon dioxide there is   number of rocks in a field   temperature   how much water there is   amount of light   day of the week

Q3 Dan wanted to investigate the number of **daisies** on his school field. He placed a 1 m² quadrat down at **eight random points** in the field. Then he counted the number of daisies in each quadrat. He recorded his results in the table shown below.

Quadrat number	1	2	3	4	5	6	7	8
Number of daisies	3	1	2	1	4	3	0	2

a) Suggest **one** way that Dan could make sure his quadrats are placed at random points.

....

....

b) i) Calculate the mean number of daisies per quadrat in the field.

$$\text{mean} = \frac{\text{total number of organisms}}{\text{total number of quadrats}}$$

....

ii) The total area of the field is 5 600 m². Use the equation below and your answer to **b) i)** to estimate the number of daisies in the whole field.

population size = mean number of organisms per 1 m² quadrat × total area (in m²)

....

c) What is the median number of daisies per quadrat?

....

Top Tips: Some questions may feel like you're doing maths rather than biology... but you can't get away from things like the mean — you do need to know how to work them out for the exam. Booo.

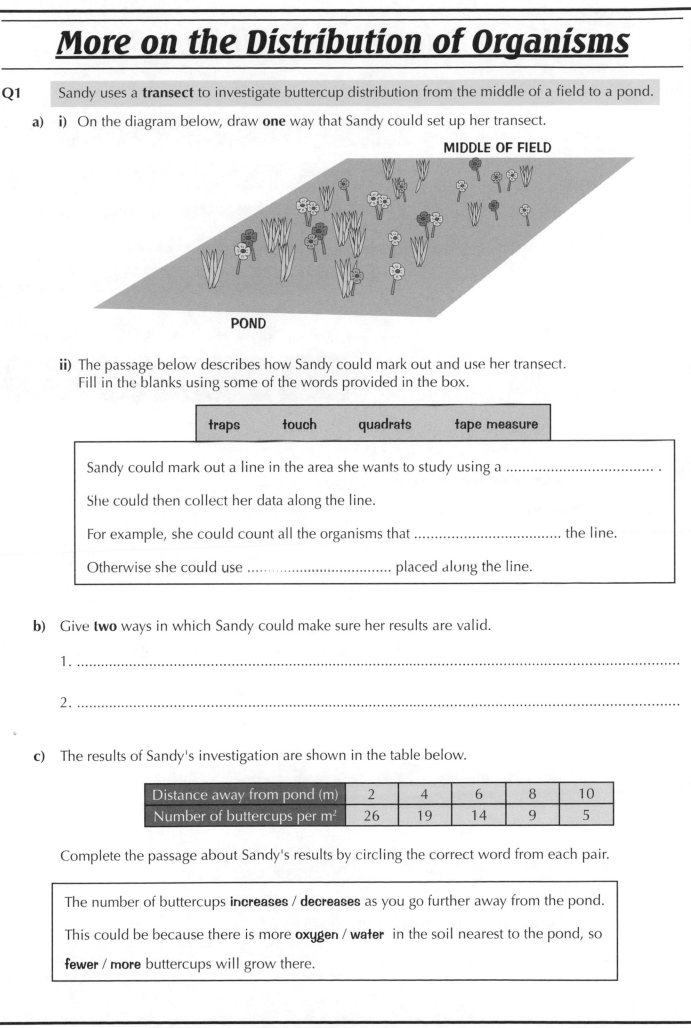

More on the Distribution of Organisms

Q1 Sandy uses a **transect** to investigate buttercup distribution from the middle of a field to a pond.

a) **i)** On the diagram below, draw **one** way that Sandy could set up her transect.

MIDDLE OF FIELD

POND

ii) The passage below describes how Sandy could mark out and use her transect.
Fill in the blanks using some of the words provided in the box.

| traps | touch | quadrats | tape measure |

Sandy could mark out a line in the area she wants to study using a ....

She could then collect her data along the line.

For example, she could count all the organisms that .... the line.

Otherwise she could use .... placed along the line.

b) Give **two** ways in which Sandy could make sure her results are valid.

1. ....

2. ....

c) The results of Sandy's investigation are shown in the table below.

Distance away from pond (m)	2	4	6	8	10
Number of buttercups per m²	26	19	14	9	5

Complete the passage about Sandy's results by circling the correct word from each pair.

The number of buttercups **increases / decreases** as you go further away from the pond.

This could be because there is more **oxygen / water** in the soil nearest to the pond, so **fewer / more** buttercups will grow there.

Mixed Questions — Biology 2a

Q1 Draw lines to match up the words below with their correct definition.

Organ

Diffusion

Mode

Photosynthesis

Limiting factor

Differentiation

The process that produces 'food' (glucose) in plants and algae.

Something that stops photosynthesis from going any faster.

A group of different tissues that work together to perform a certain function.

The process by which a cell changes to become specialised.

The most common value in a set of data.

The spreading out of particles from an area of high concentration to an area of low concentration.

Q2 Cells in **plants** are different from cells in animals.

a) Name **three** parts that are found in plant cells but **not** in animal cells.

1. ....

2. ....

3. ....

b) Complete this diagram of a plant cell by filling in the labels. One has been done for you.

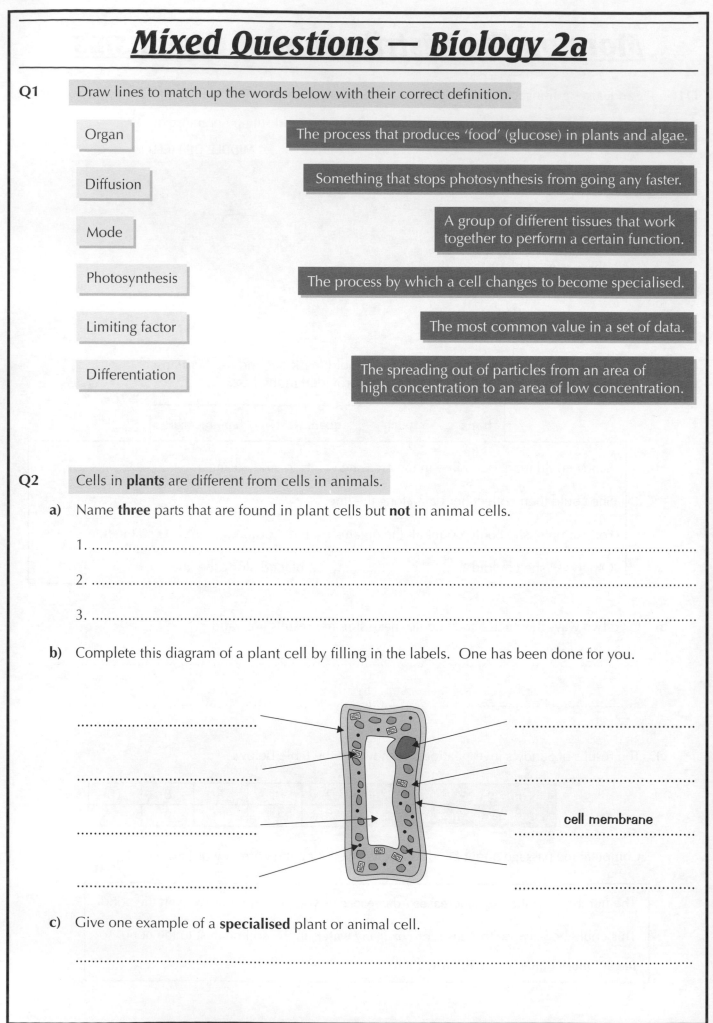

....

....

....

....

....

cell membrane

....

c) Give one example of a **specialised** plant or animal cell.

....

Mixed Questions — Biology 2a

Q3 Plants use photosynthesis to produce glucose.

a) Name the substance in a plant that absorbs light energy during photosynthesis.

....

b) Circle **two** raw materials needed for photosynthesis from the options given below.

carbon dioxide   oxygen   food   water   nitrogen   helium

c) Give **three uses** of glucose for plants.

1. ....

2. ....

3. ....

Q4 Some students wanted to estimate the size of the population of **clover plants** around their school.

a) **i)** The school field is 250 m long by 180 m wide. What is the area of the school field?

....

....

Area is just length times width.

ii) Hannah counted 11 clover plants in a 1 m² area of the field.
Approximately how many clover plants are there likely to be on the whole field?

....

....

Take a look back at page 12 to see how to work out population size.

b) Lisa decided to collect data from five different 1 m² areas of the school field. Her results are shown in the table below.

	Area 1	Area 2	Area 3	Area 4	Area 5
No. of plants	11	9	8	9	7

i) Calculate the **mean** number of clover plants per m² in Lisa's survey.

....

ii) Use Lisa's data to estimate the population size of clover plants on the field.

....

c) Whose estimation of population size is likely to be more accurate? Explain your answer.

....

Enzymes

Q1 What is a **catalyst**? Tick **two** correct boxes below.

A substance that speeds up chemical reactions. ☐

A substance that slows down chemical reactions. ☐

A substance that is changed in a reaction. ☐

A substance that is not changed or used up in a reaction. ☐

Q2 Some statements about **chemical reactions** are written below.
Decide which are correct and then write **true** or **false** in the spaces.

a) We have lots of chemical reactions going on inside us all the time. ....

b) Chemical reactions only ever involve things being split up. ....

c) One enzyme can catalyse many different types of reaction. ....

d) Every enzyme has a specific shape. ....

Q3 a) What is an 'enzyme'? Circle the correct answer.

a biological catalyst   a cell structure   an artificial catalyst   a type of organ

b) Complete the diagram below to show how an enzyme breaks down a substance.

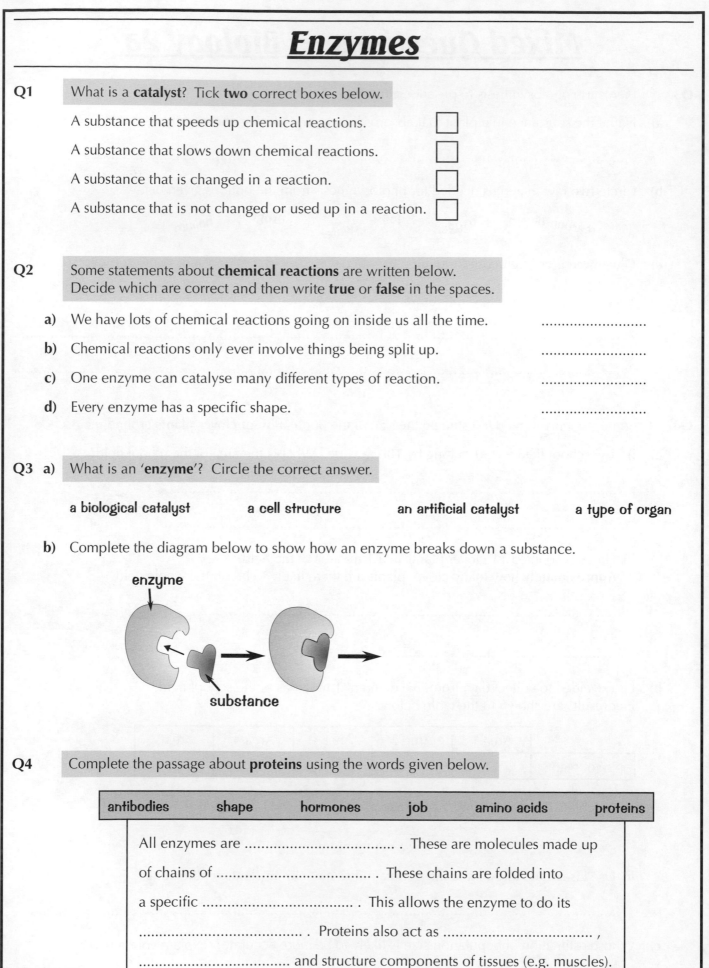

enzyme

substance

Q4 Complete the passage about **proteins** using the words given below.

antibodies	shape	hormones	job	amino acids	proteins

All enzymes are .... These are molecules made up

of chains of .... These chains are folded into

a specific .... This allows the enzyme to do its

.... Proteins also act as .... ,

.... and structure components of tissues (e.g. muscles).

More on Enzymes

Q1 This graph shows the results from an investigation into the effect of **temperature** on the rate of an **enzyme** catalysed reaction.

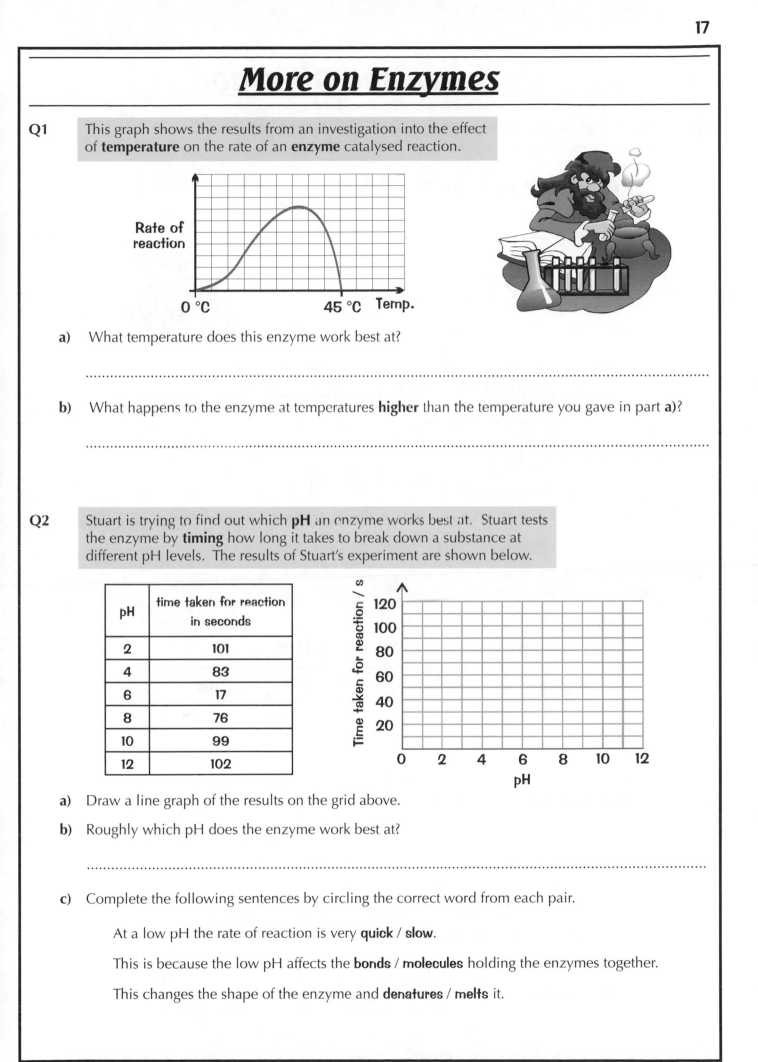

a) What temperature does this enzyme work best at?

....

b) What happens to the enzyme at temperatures **higher** than the temperature you gave in part **a)**?

....

Q2 Stuart is trying to find out which **pH** an enzyme works best at. Stuart tests the enzyme by **timing** how long it takes to break down a substance at different pH levels. The results of Stuart's experiment are shown below.

pH	time taken for reaction in seconds
2	101
4	83
6	17
8	76
10	99
12	102

a) Draw a line graph of the results on the grid above.

b) Roughly which pH does the enzyme work best at?

....

c) Complete the following sentences by circling the correct word from each pair.

At a low pH the rate of reaction is very **quick / slow**.

This is because the low pH affects the **bonds / molecules** holding the enzymes together.

This changes the shape of the enzyme and **denatures / melts** it.

Biology 2b — Enzymes and Genetics

Enzymes and Digestion

Q1 The flow chart shows how the **three main food groups** are **broken down** during digestion. Use the words below to fill in the boxes.

sugars   protease   amylase   fatty acids   amino acids   glycerol   fat

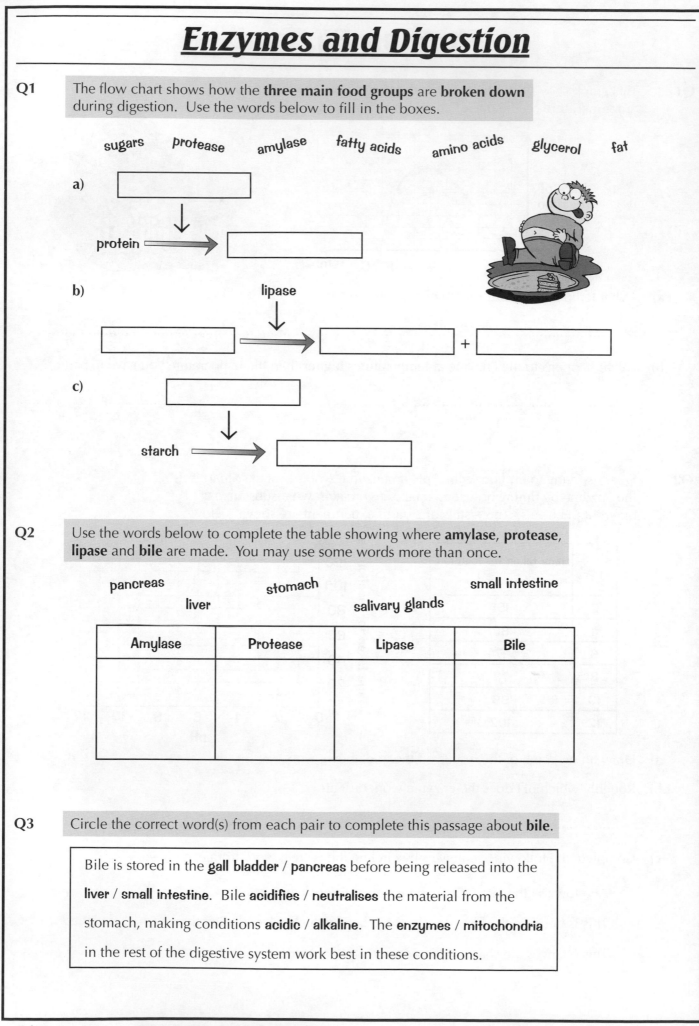

a)

[ ]

protein → [ ]

b)

lipase

[ ] → [ ] + [ ]

c)

[ ]

starch → [ ]

Q2 Use the words below to complete the table showing where **amylase**, **protease**, **lipase** and **bile** are made. You may use some words more than once.

pancreas   stomach   small intestine
        liver   salivary glands

Amylase	Protease	Lipase	Bile

Q3 Circle the correct word(s) from each pair to complete this passage about **bile**.

Bile is stored in the **gall bladder / pancreas** before being released into the **liver / small intestine**. Bile **acidifies / neutralises** the material from the stomach, making conditions **acidic / alkaline**. The **enzymes / mitochondria** in the rest of the digestive system work best in these conditions.

Enzymes and Respiration

Q1 a) Circle the correct word equation for **aerobic respiration**.

glucose + oxygen → carbon dioxide + water (+ energy)

protein + oxygen → carbon dioxide + water (+ energy)

glucose + carbon dioxide → oxygen + water (+ energy)

b) Complete the sentence to explain what '**aerobic respiration**' means.

Aerobic respiration is respiration using ....

Q2 a) Tick the correct boxes to show whether the sentences are **true** or **false**.

True False

i) Aerobic respiration produces carbon dioxide. ☐ ☐

ii) Breathing is a kind of respiration. ☐ ☐

iii) Respiration goes on all the time in both plants and animals. ☐ ☐

iv) Respiration involves reactions catalysed by enzymes. ☐ ☐

b) Where in a cell does aerobic respiration take place? Circle the correct answer.

cytoplasm   mitochondria   nucleus   ribosomes   chloroplasts

Q3 a) Fill in the blanks in the paragraph below using words from the list.

muscles   sugars   larger   amino acids   proteins

Aerobic respiration releases energy for all kinds of things, including:

• Building up .... molecules from smaller ones.

• In animals, allowing the .... to contract.

• In plants, building ...., nitrates and other nutrients into amino acids. These are then used to build ....

b) Give **one** other way mammals and birds use the energy from aerobic respiration.

....

___

Top Tips: Hmm, respiration, there isn't really much to say other than make sure you learn the word equation and remember that IT'S NOT THE SAME AS BREATHING.

Biology 2b — Enzymes and Genetics

Exercise

Q1 Complete the following sentences by circling the correct words from each pair.

a) During exercise our muscles need more **energy** / **water** to enable them to keep **relaxing** / **contracting**.

b) This means they need more **protein** / **glucose** and **carbon dioxide** / **oxygen**.

c) During exercise extra **carbon dioxide** / **nitrogen** needs to be removed from the muscle cells.

d) During exercise your blood needs to flow **faster** / **slower** to get substances to and from your cells.

e) If your body can't supply enough oxygen to the muscles during exercise they start using **aerobic** / **anaerobic** respiration.

Q2 Circle the correct word(s) to complete each sentence.

a) Your muscles .... glucose as glycogen.

         absorb   **release**   **store**

b) i) During hard exercise, muscles use glucose ....

      slowly   **quickly**   **at the same rate as normal**

    ii) This means the glycogen is changed back into glucose

      to give more ....

      proteins   **energy**   **glycerol**   **starch**

Q3 John has to **sprint** for the bus because he is late.

a) State **two** effects this sudden physical exercise has on John's body.

    1. ....

    2. ....

b) After his sprint, John's leg muscles become tired and stop contracting as well.

    i) What name is given to this effect? Tick the right box.

      muscle burnout ☐   **arthritis** ☐   **muscle fatigue** ☐   **tendonitis** ☐

    ii) Suggest the substance that is causing this effect.

      ....

Exercise

Q4 Anaerobic respiration is a type of respiration.

a) What is anaerobic respiration? Circle the correct answer.

It is respiration without glucose.   It is respiration with starch.   It is respiration with carbon dioxide.   It is respiration without oxygen.

b) Name **one** chemical produced by anaerobic respiration.

....

Q5 Jim is a keen runner. He takes part in a 400 metre race. The **graph** below shows Jim's **breathing rate** before, during and after the race.

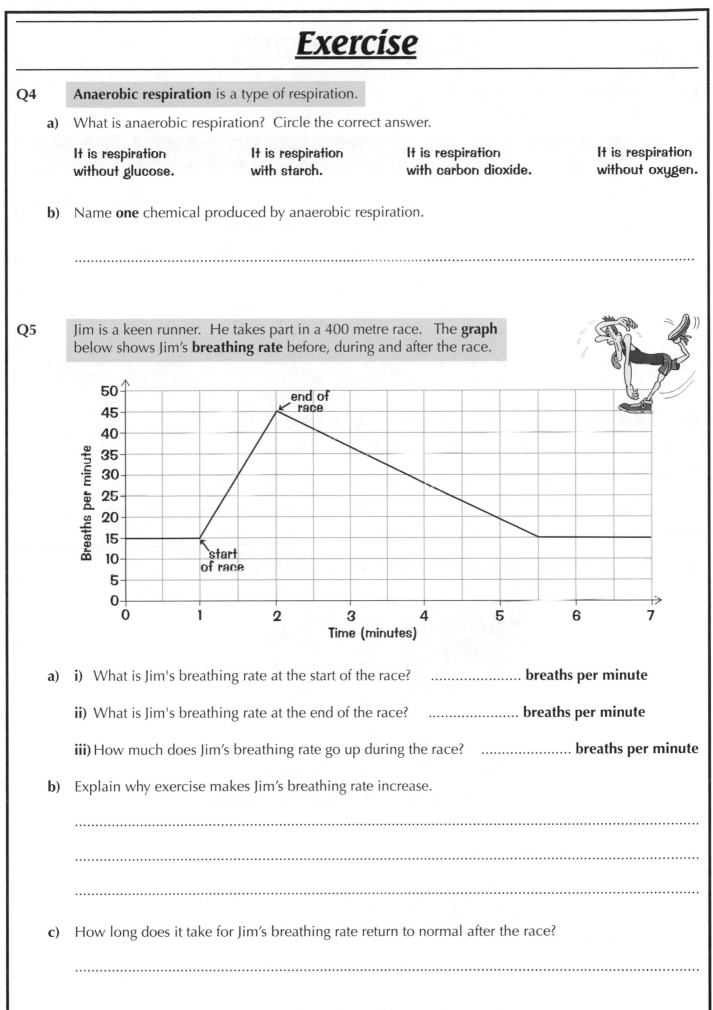

a) i) What is Jim's breathing rate at the start of the race? .... breaths per minute

ii) What is Jim's breathing rate at the end of the race? .... breaths per minute

iii) How much does Jim's breathing rate go up during the race? .... breaths per minute

b) Explain why exercise makes Jim's breathing rate increase.

....

....

....

c) How long does it take for Jim's breathing rate return to normal after the race?

....

Biology 2b — Enzymes and Genetics

Uses of Enzymes

Q1 **Enzymes** are often used in industrial processes to change foods.
Complete the passage below using the words in the box.

| sweeter | proteases | isomerase | pre-digested | fructose | easier | less | slimming |

The proteins in some baby foods are .... — they've already been broken

down using .... This means they're .... for the

baby to digest. Glucose syrup can be turned into .... syrup using

an .... enzyme. This syrup is .... than glucose

syrup. This means you can use .... of it — making it good for using

in .... foods and drinks.

Q2 Complete the following sentences by circling the correct words.

a) Starch and sugar are both **proteins** / **carbohydrates** / **fats**.

b) Starch syrup **is** / **isn't** sweet. Sugar syrup **is** / **isn't** sweet.

c) You can convert starch syrup into sugar syrup by adding **lipases** / **carbohydrases** / **proteases**.

Q3 The picture below shows two types of biological **washing powders**.

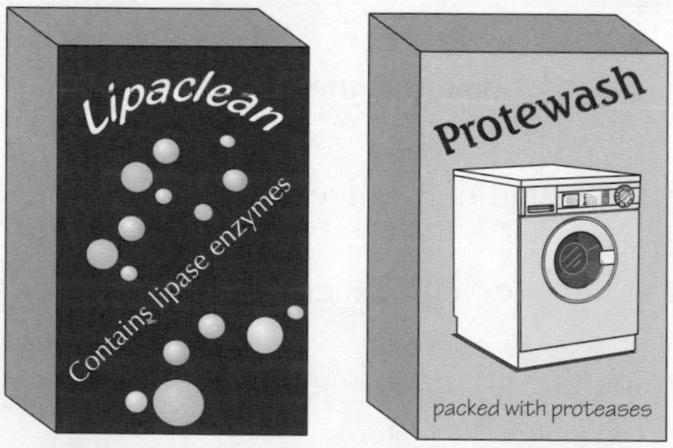

a) What do the washing powders above contain that other 'non-biological' types
of washing powders do not?

   ....

b) Mark dripped some butter on his shirt.
Suggest why he should use Lipaclean to clean his shirt instead of Protewash.

   ....

   ....

Uses of Enzymes

Q4 **Enzymes** are often used in **industrial processes**.

a) Why are enzymes used in industrial processes? Circle the correct answer.

| To slow down reactions. | To speed up reactions. | To increase the cost of processes. | To increase the temperature of processes. |

b) i) Give **one advantage** of using enzymes in industry.

....

....

ii) Give **one disadvantage** of using enzymes in industry.

....

....

Q5 Caroline is testing how good two different **washing powders** are at getting out food stains. She washes stained clothes in both powders, at different temperatures. Then she records how well they worked using a scale of **1** (**poor**) to **10** (**excellent**).

a) Name **one** thing that Caroline must do to make sure that her experiment is a fair test.

....

b) Caroline's results are shown in the table below.

	Washing powder	
	A	B
Temperature: 20 °C	5	2
Temperature: 30 °C	8	4
Temperature: 40 °C	9	6

Score (label on left)

i) Which powder is best at cleaning food stains at **30 °C**? Tick the correct box.

☐ Powder A   ☐ Powder B

ii) Which of the powders is a **biological washing powder**? Explain your answer.

....

....

Think about what temperatures biological washing powders work best at.

Top Tips: Each enzyme catalyses a specific reaction, e.g. proteases break down proteins. This means enzymes can be really useful, e.g. proteases are put in washing powders. However, when using them, you have to keep conditions tightly controlled otherwise they will be denatured.

DNA

Q1 DNA contains all the **instructions** to make an living organism.

a) What does DNA stand for? Circle the correct answer.

deoxyribonucleic acid   disulfurnucleic acid   dicarboxylicnucliec acid

b) Fill in the blanks in the paragraph below using words from the list.

nucleus   section   chromosomes   cells   long

DNA is found in the .... of animal and plant ....

It is found in very .... molecules called ....

A gene is a .... of DNA.

c) DNA molecules have a special twisted structure. Give the name of this structure.

....

d) Is everyone's DNA unique? Explain your answer.

....

Q2 A horse breeder has collected DNA samples from each of her horses. Her **new foal's DNA** is **sample 1**. The **mother** of the foal provided **sample 2**. Study the **DNA fingerprints** and complete the table showing which horse is the **foal's father**.

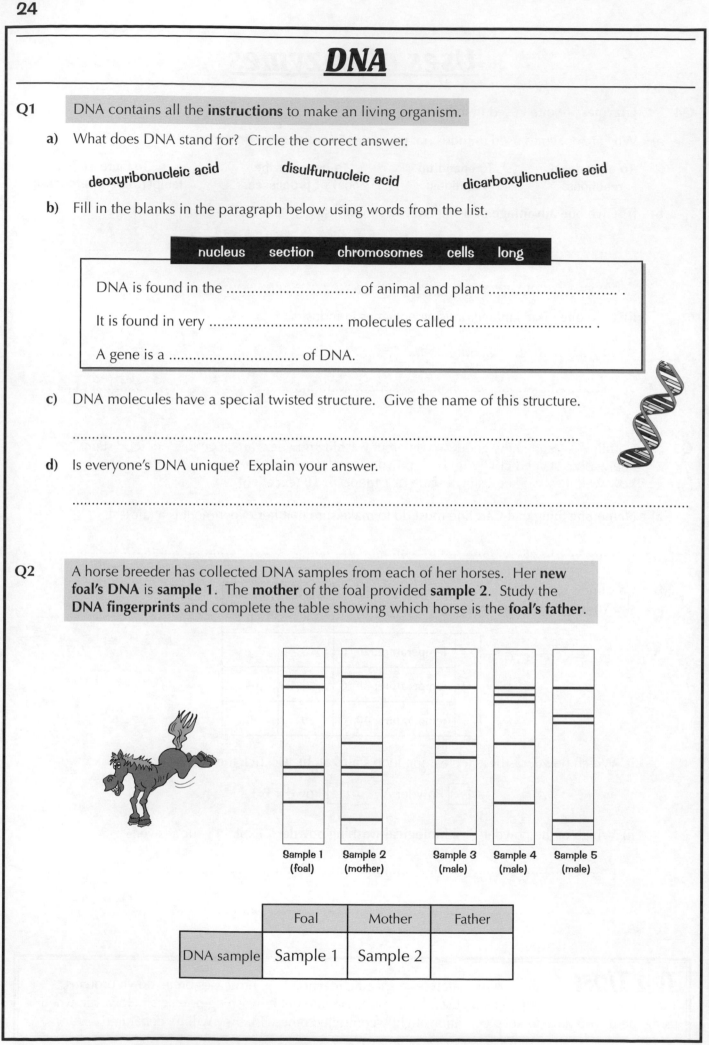

Sample 1 (foal)   Sample 2 (mother)   Sample 3 (male)   Sample 4 (male)   Sample 5 (male)

	Foal	Mother	Father
DNA sample	Sample 1	Sample 2	

Mitosis

Q1   Decide whether the following statements are **true** or **false**.

	True	False

a)   Body cells divide by mitosis.

b)   There are 20 pairs of chromosomes in a human cheek cell.

c)   Before a cell divides by mitosis, it copies its DNA.

d)   Mitosis produces new cells to replace those which are damaged.

e)   We need mitosis to grow.

f)   In mitosis a cell divides twice.

g)   Mitosis only happens in humans.

Q2   Complete the sentence by ticking the correct box below.

Mitosis is when a cell copies itself by splitting to form...

...four genetically different offspring. ☐

...two identical offspring. ☐

...two genetically different offspring. ☐

...four identical offspring. ☐

Q3   The following diagrams show the different stages of **mitosis**.
Draw lines to match the description of each stage with the correct diagram.

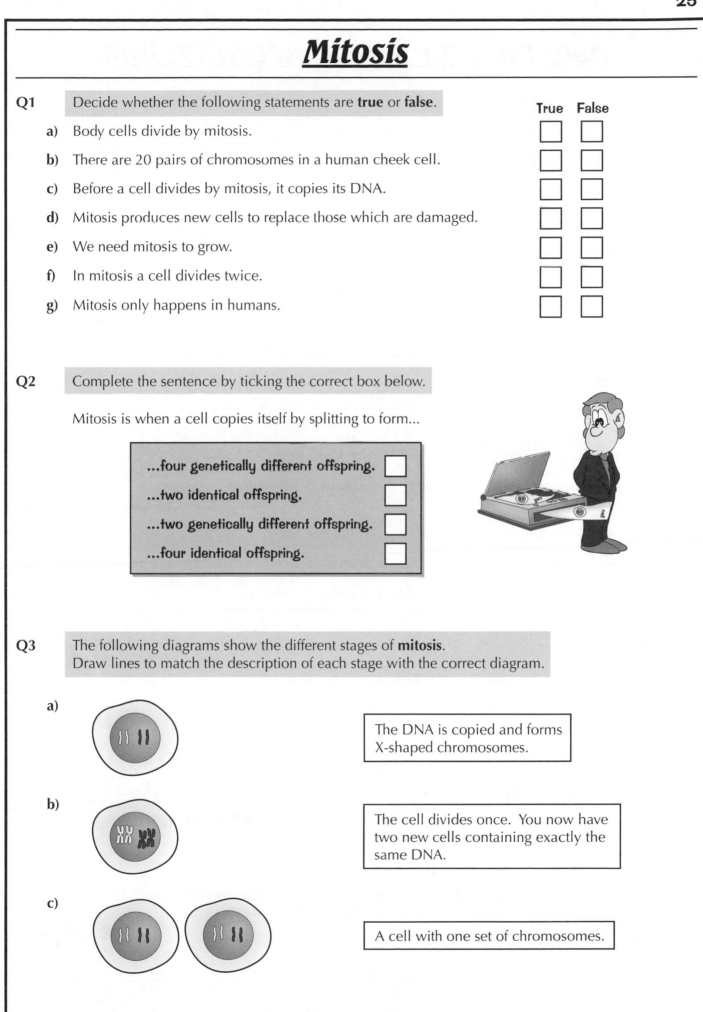

a)

The DNA is copied and forms X-shaped chromosomes.

b)

The cell divides once. You now have two new cells containing exactly the same DNA.

c)

A cell with one set of chromosomes.

Biology 2b — Enzymes and Genetics

Asexual and Sexual Reproduction

Q1 Tick the boxes below to show whether the following statements are true or false.

True **False**

a) In humans, meiosis only happens in the reproductive organs. ☐ ☐

b) Meiosis doesn't form gametes. ☐ ☐

c) Meiosis forms cells that have two sets of chromosomes. ☐ ☐

Q2 Circle the correct words to complete the sentences below.

a) Sexual reproduction involves chromosomes from **one** / **two** individual(s).

b) In humans, body cells contain **46** / **23** chromosomes and sex cells contain **46** / **23** chromosomes.

c) Sexual reproduction produces offspring with **identical** / **different** genes to the parents.

d) The sperm cell contains **the same number of** / **half as many** chromosomes as the fertilised egg.

Q3 Complete the following passage using the words below.

strawberry   variation   asexual   reproduce   genes

Some organisms .... by mitosis. For example, ... plants.

This is known as .... reproduction. The offspring have exactly the same

.... as the parent, so there's no genetic ....

Q4 At fertilisation, two **gametes** combine to form a new individual.

a) What are gametes?

....

b) Which of the following is the correct explanation of how sexual reproduction gives rise to **variation**? Tick the right box.

☐ The new individual will have a mixture of two sets of chromosomes. This means it will inherit features from both parents.

☐ Fertilisation changes an individual's genes, which causes variation.

☐ The new individual will only inherit it's mother's chromosomes. This means it will only inherit features from its mother.

c) After fertilisation, by what process does the fertilised egg divide?

....

Stem Cells

Q1 Complete the following passage about **differentiation** using words from the list below.

| plant | specialised | stem | animal |

Differentiation is the process by which a cell changes to become ....

for its job. In most .... cells the ability to differentiate is lost at an

early stage. But lots of .... cells don't ever lose this ability.

Some cells are undifferentiated. They can develop into different types of cells.

These cells are called .... cells.

Q2 **Embryonic stem cells** are different from **adult stem cells**.
Draw lines to match the type of stem cell below to its description.

Adult stem cells

Embryonic stem cells

These stem cells can turn into many cell types (but not all cell types).

These stem cells have the potential to turn into ANY kind of cell.

Q3 In the future, **stem cells** might be used to replace faulty cells in sick people.

Which of the following cells would a scientist use to replace faulty cells in a paralysed person? Circle the correct answer.

insulin-producing cells   heart muscle cells   nerve cells

Q4 People have **different opinions** when it comes to **stem cell research**.

a) Give **one** argument **in favour** of stem cell research.

....

....

b) Give **one** argument **against** stem cell research.

....

....

X and Y Chromosomes

Q1 Tick the boxes to show whether each statement is **true** or **false**.

True False

a) Women have two X chromosomes.

b) Men have an X and a Y chromosome.

c) Sperm cells (male gametes) can carry an X or a Y chromosome.

d) Egg cells (female gametes) can carry an X or a Y chromosome.

e) If you have 4 children, you will always get 2 boys and 2 girls.

Q2 Here is a genetic diagram showing the inheritance of **sex chromosomes** in humans.

a) Complete the diagram to show the combinations of chromosomes in the offspring.

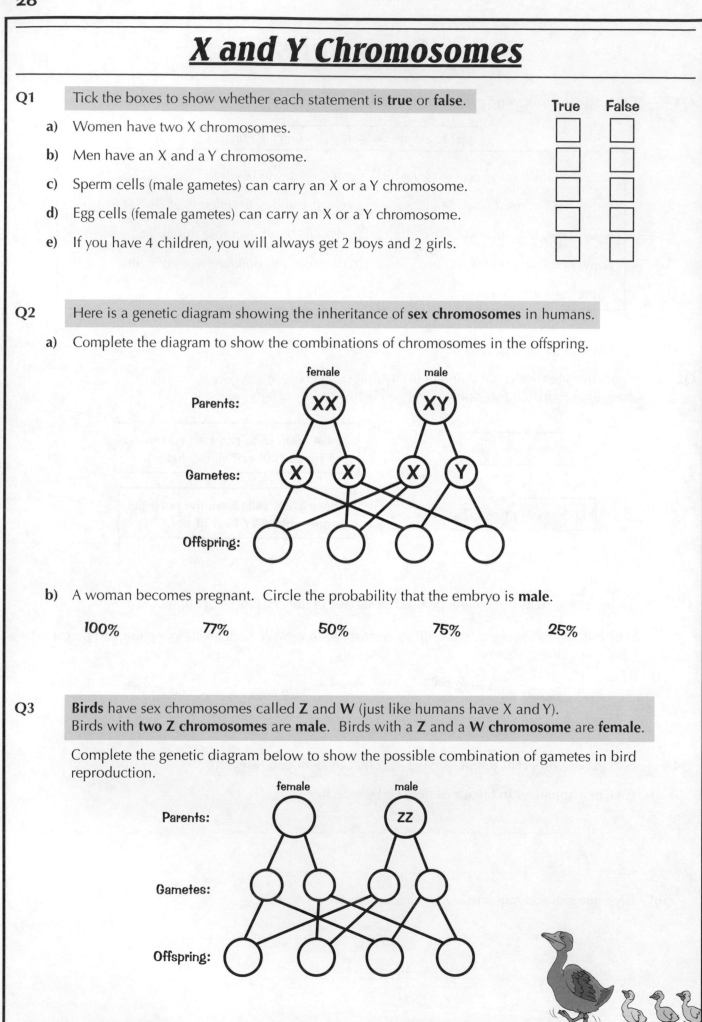

female   male

Parents: XX   XY

Gametes: X   X   X   Y

Offspring:

b) A woman becomes pregnant. Circle the probability that the embryo is **male**.

100%   77%   50%   75%   25%

Q3 **Birds** have sex chromosomes called **Z** and **W** (just like humans have X and Y).
Birds with **two Z chromosomes** are **male**. Birds with a **Z** and a **W chromosome** are **female**.

Complete the genetic diagram below to show the possible combination of gametes in bird reproduction.

female   male

Parents: ZZ

Gametes:

Offspring:

Genetic Diagrams

Q1   Complete the following sentences by circling the correct word from each pair.

a)   Alleles are different versions of the same **gene** / **gamete**.

b)   These alleles give **different** / **the same** versions of a characteristic.

c)   You have **two** / **three** alleles for each gene.

Q2   Draw lines to match the statements below with the correct endings.

| If you have one dominant allele and one recessive allele... | ... the recessive characteristic will be shown. |

| If you have two recessive alleles... | ... the dominant characteristic will be shown. |

Q3   Fruit flies usually have **red** eyes. However, there are a small number of white-eyed fruit flies. Having **white** eyes is a **recessive** characteristic.

a)   Complete the following sentences with either '**red eyes**' or '**white eyes**'.

i) **R** is the allele for ....

ii) **r** is the allele for ....

iii) Fruit flies with alleles **RR** or **Rr** will have ....

iv) Fruit flies with the alleles **rr** will have ....

b)   Two fruit flies have the alleles **Rr**. They fall in love and get it on.

i)   Complete this genetic diagram to show the possible offspring. One's been done for you.

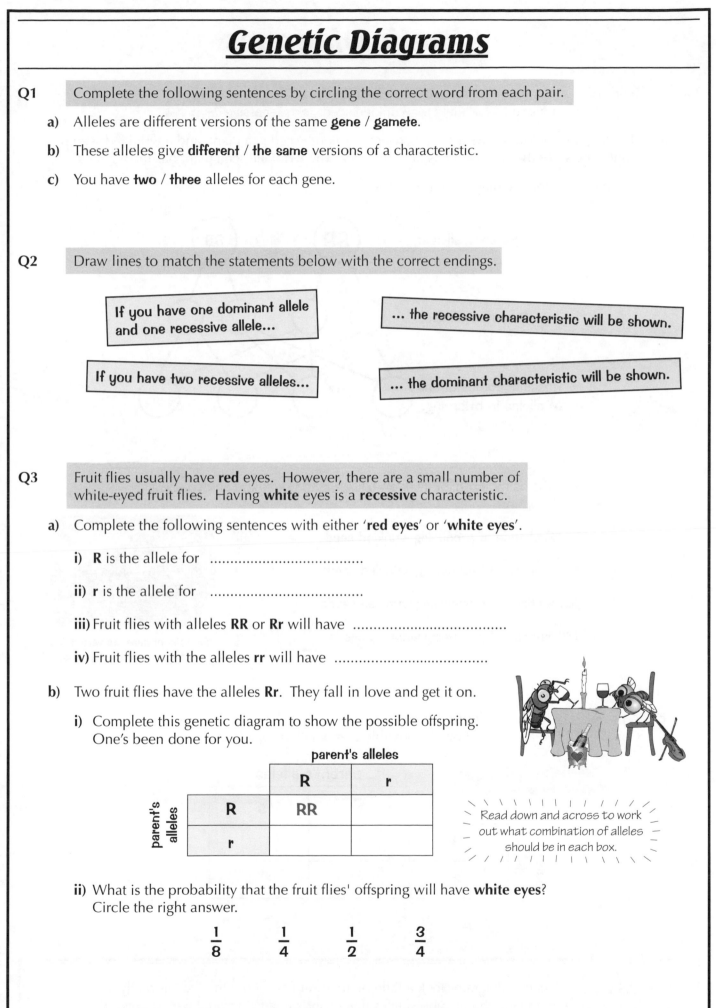

parent's alleles

		R	r
parent's alleles	**R**	RR	
	r		

Read down and across to work out what combination of alleles should be in each box.

ii) What is the probability that the fruit flies' offspring will have **white eyes**? Circle the right answer.

$$\frac{1}{8} \qquad \frac{1}{4} \qquad \frac{1}{2} \qquad \frac{3}{4}$$

Genetic Diagrams

Q4 Seeds of pea plants can be **smooth** or **wrinkled**. The allele for smooth
seeds (**S**) is dominant. The allele for wrinkled seeds (**s**) is recessive.

a) The diagrams below shows a cross between a smooth seed pea plant, and a wrinkled seed pea
plant. The **smooth** seed plant has the alleles **SS**. The **wrinkled** seed plant has the alleles **ss**.

Complete the genetic diagram for this cross.

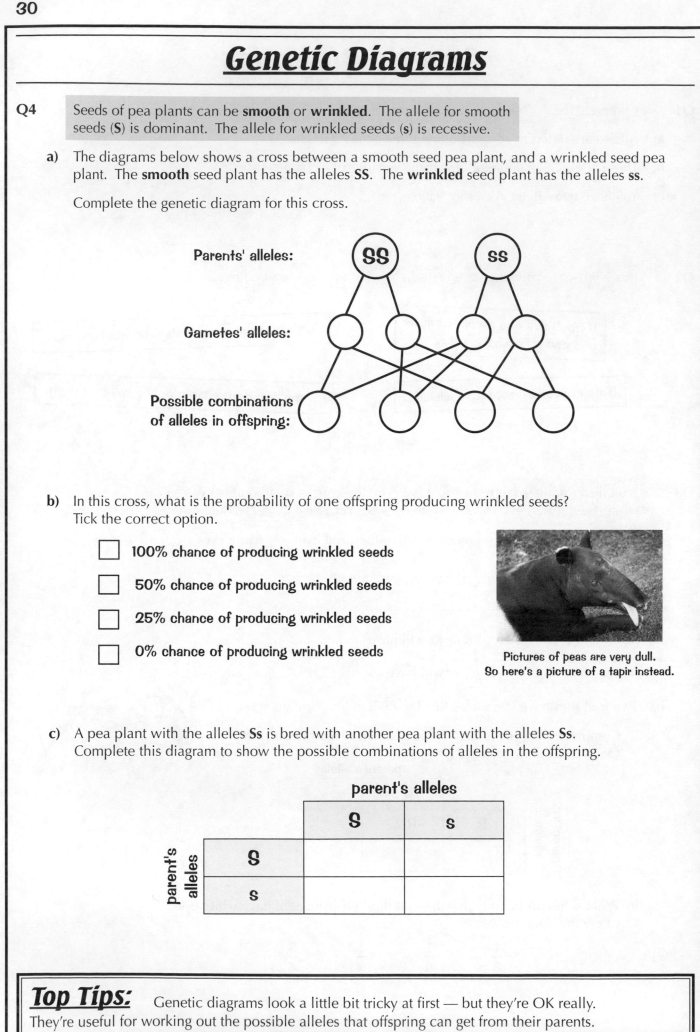

Parents' alleles:

Gametes' alleles:

Possible combinations
of alleles in offspring:

b) In this cross, what is the probability of one offspring producing wrinkled seeds?
Tick the correct option.

☐ 100% chance of producing wrinkled seeds

☐ 50% chance of producing wrinkled seeds

☐ 25% chance of producing wrinkled seeds

☐ 0% chance of producing wrinkled seeds

Pictures of peas are very dull.
So here's a picture of a tapir instead.

c) A pea plant with the alleles **Ss** is bred with another pea plant with the alleles **Ss**.
Complete this diagram to show the possible combinations of alleles in the offspring.

		parent's alleles	
		S	s
parent's alleles	S		
	s		

Top Tips: Genetic diagrams look a little bit tricky at first — but they're OK really.
They're useful for working out the possible alleles that offspring can get from their parents.

Biology 2b — Enzymes and Genetics

The Work of Mendel

Q1 Use words from the following list to complete the paragraph below.

monk   1866   parents   characteristics   1980   inherited

Gregor Mendel was a .... Mendel observed plants in his garden. He realised that .... in plants are determined by .... units. These units are passed on from both .... to their offspring. He published his findings in ....

Q2 Mendel crossed different combinations of **tall** and **dwarf** pea plants.

a) Complete the genetic diagrams below showing crossings of different pea plants.
T represents the dominant allele for **tall plants** and **t** represents the recessive allele for **dwarf plants**.

Cross 1:

tall   dwarf

parents: TT   tt

T   T   t   t

offspring: Tt   Tt   ◯   ◯

tall   tall   ....

Cross 2:

tall   tall

parents: Tt   Tt

◯   ◯   ◯   ◯

offspring: ◯   ◯   ◯   ◯

....

b) In **cross 2**, what is the probability of one of the offspring plants being tall?

....

Tall pea plants must have the alleles TT or Tt.

Genetic Disorders

Q1   **Genetic disorders** can be passed on from parents to children in their genes.

a)   Cystic fibrosis is caused by a recessive allele, **f**. The dominant allele is **F**.
     The box below shows the names of three people and their alleles.

Peter, ff	Anna, FF	Hamid, Ff

   i) **Circle** the name of **one** person who **suffers** from cystic fibrosis.

   ii) **Underline** the name of **one** person who is a **carrier** of cystic fibrosis but does not suffer from it.

b)   Polydactyly is caused by a dominant allele, **D**. The recessive allele is **d**.
     The box below shows the names of three people and their alleles.

Kelly, Dd	Sara, dd	Mark, DD

   i) **Circle** the name of **one** person who **suffers** from polydactyly.

   ii) **Underline** the name of **one** person who **does not suffer** polydactyly.

Q2   Faulty genes can cause genetic disorders, such as **cystic fibrosis**.

a)   What part of a cell does cystic fibrosis affect? Circle the correct answer.

   nucleus   mitochondria   cell wells   cell membranes

b)   Complete the following genetic diagram showing the inheritance of cystic fibrosis.
     The recessive allele for cystic fibrosis is **f**, and the dominant allele is **F**.

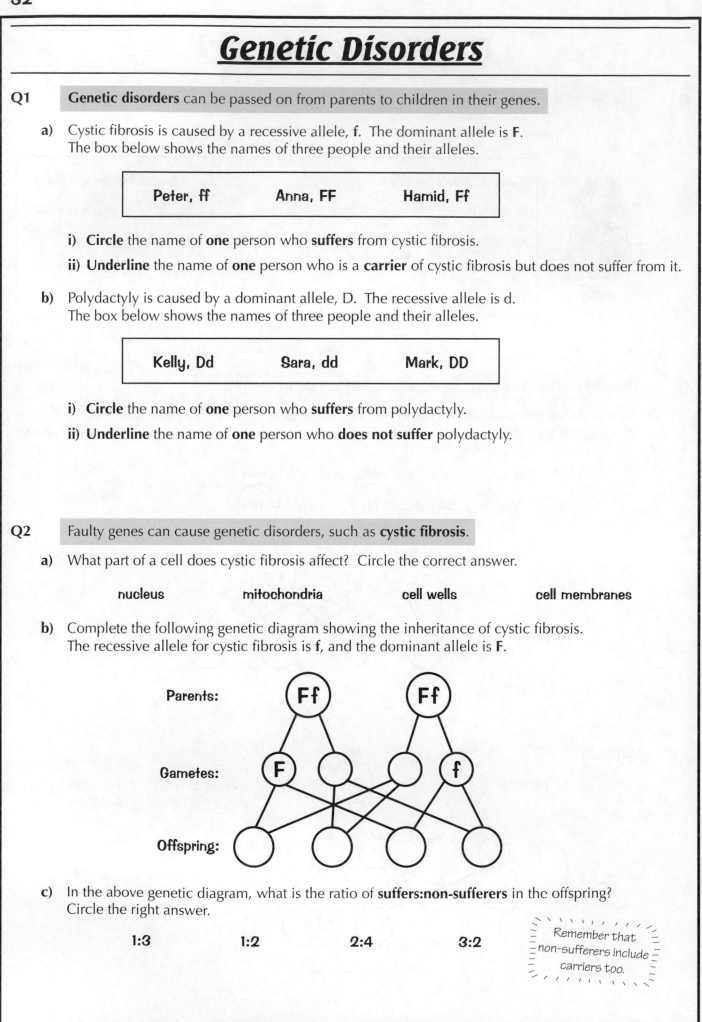

c)   In the above genetic diagram, what is the ratio of **suffers:non-sufferers** in the offspring?
     Circle the right answer.

   1:3   1:2   2:4   3:2

Remember that non-sufferers include carriers too.

Genetic Disorders

Q3 **Cystic fibrosis** is a **recessive** genetic disorder. John is a carrier of cystic fibrosis. His wife Helen is **not** a carrier of cystic fibrosis (and does not suffer from the disease).

John and Helen are planning a family.

a) Complete the genetic diagram below to show what alleles their child might inherit from them. Use the symbols **F** and **f** to represent the alleles.

Use the information in the introduction to work out what alleles John and Helen will have.

Helen's alleles

	....	....
John's alleles	....	....
....	....	....

b) What is the probability that John and Helen's child will suffer from cystic fibrosis?

....

Think of the alleles that a person with cystic fibrosis will have.

Q4 **Polydactyly** is a **genetic disorder**. It is caused by a **dominant** allele.

a) How can polydactyly affect a person?

....

b) Complete the genetic diagram below showing the inheritance pattern of polydactyly. The dominant allele for polydactyly is **D**, and the recessive allele is **d**.

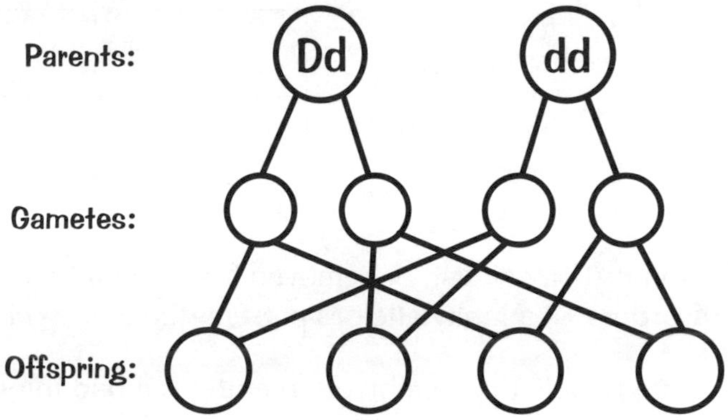

Parents: Dd dd

Gametes:

Offspring:

c) Will a person with the alleles **Dd** be a **sufferer**, a **carrier** or **neither**? Circle the correct answer.

sufferer   carrier   neither

Explain your answer.

....

Family Trees and Embryo Screening

Q1 The family tree below shows a family with a history of **cystic fibrosis**.

a) Explain how you can tell from the family tree that the allele for cystic fibrosis is **not** dominant.

....

....

Libby is pregnant. She doesn't know if the baby will have cystic fibrosis.

b) i) From the family tree work out what alleles Libby and Drew must have.
Use **F** as the dominant allele and **f** as the recessive allele.

....

ii) Complete the genetic diagram to show what alleles their child might inherit.

Fill in the alleles you worked out for Libby and Drew in part i) first.

Libby's alleles

		....	....
Drew's alleles	....	....	....
	....	....	....

Q2 During in vitro fertilisation (IVF) a cell can be removed from an embryo and **screened** for **genetic disorders**. If a faulty allele is present, the embryo is destroyed.

a) Give **one** reason why some people think embryo screening is a **bad** thing.

....

....

b) Give **one** reason why some people think embryo screening is a **good** thing.

....

....

Fossils

Q1 Scientists can use **fossils** to study what life on Earth used to be like.

a) What are fossils? Tick the correct box.

- [ ] The remains of organisms from last week.
- [ ] The remains of organisms from many years ago.
- [ ] The bones of organisms from many years ago that have turned into amber.

b) Complete the sentence by ticking the correct box below.

Fossils are usually found...

- [ ] ... buried in soft soil.
- [ ] ... in tree trunks.
- [ ] ... in rocks.

Q2 The hard parts of animals can become **fossils**. The sentences below describe how this happens. Circle the correct words to complete the sentences.

a) Things like teeth, shells and bones **decay easily / don't decay easily**.

b) This means they last a **long / short** time when buried.

c) When they decay they are replaced by **minerals / gases**.

d) These form a **rock-like / sand-like** substance.

e) This substance is the same **shape / colour** as the original hard part of the animal.

Q3 It can be hard to find **fossils** of very **early organisms**.

Circle **two** reasons why.

Lots of early organisms were soft-bodied, so they decayed away completely.

Most early organisms lived in the sea and fossils can't form in the sea.

Lots of early organisms were eaten before they could become fossils.

The movement of tectonic plates crushed old fossils already in the rocks.

Fossils

Q4   Choose from the words provided to complete the passage below about **fossil formation**.

cast	footprints	roots	decays	clay

Fossils can be formed when an organism is buried in a soft material

like .... This material hardens around it and the organism

.... The organism leaves a .... of itself.

An animal's burrow or a plant's .... can also be preserved

like this. Things like .... can also be pressed into

soft materials, leaving an impression when they harden.

Q5   Scientists have found **fossils** of some animals in places where there is **no oxygen**.

Tick the box next to the statement below that explains why fossils are found in these places.

- [ ] Because oxygen helps fossils to form.
- [ ] Because decay can't happen where there's no oxygen, so the animal is preserved.
- [ ] Because animals like to live where there's no oxygen, so you find their remains there.

Q6   One idea of **how life began** is that simple carbon molecules were brought to Earth by **comets**. It's not known if this is right.

a)   What do we call this type of scientific idea? Circle the correct answer below.

a hypothesis   a method   a conclusion

b)   Suggest why scientists don't know if this idea is right or not.

....

....

Think about what you need to prove whether or not an idea is right.

Top Tips: It's weird to think that looking at squiggles inside rocks can tell you what life used to be like ages ago... Don't forget to learn what fossils are and how they form.

Extinction and Speciation

Q1   Dinosaurs, mammoths and dodos are all animals that are now **extinct**.

What does it mean if a species is 'extinct'? Tick the correct box.

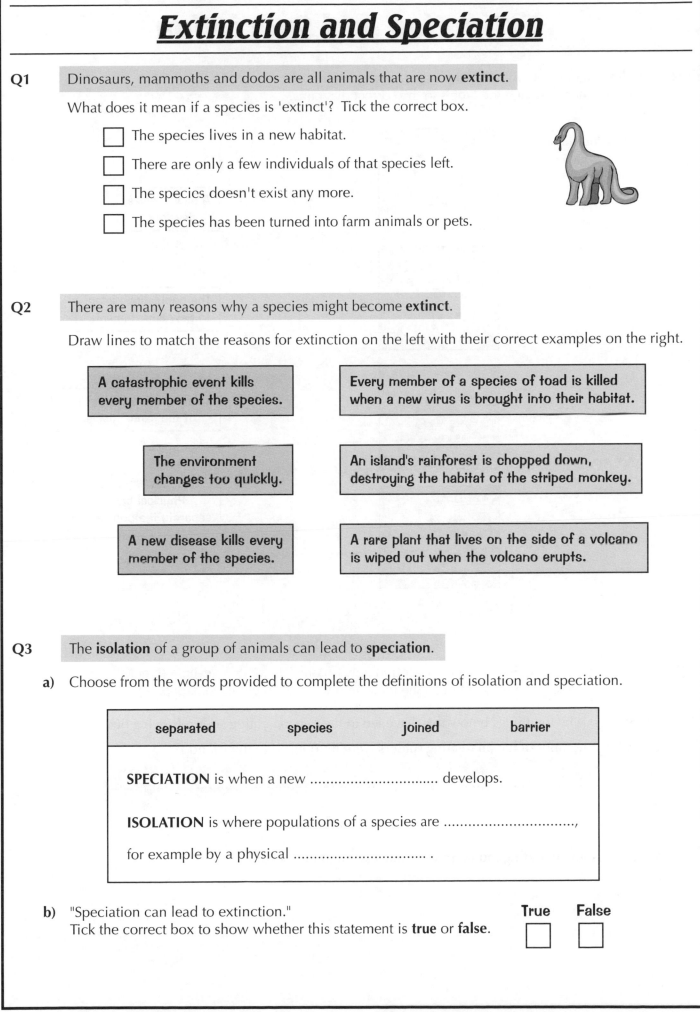

☐ The species lives in a new habitat.

☐ There are only a few individuals of that species left.

☐ The species doesn't exist any more.

☐ The species has been turned into farm animals or pets.

Q2   There are many reasons why a species might become **extinct**.

Draw lines to match the reasons for extinction on the left with their correct examples on the right.

| A catastrophic event kills every member of the species. | Every member of a species of toad is killed when a new virus is brought into their habitat. |

| The environment changes too quickly. | An island's rainforest is chopped down, destroying the habitat of the striped monkey. |

| A new disease kills every member of the species. | A rare plant that lives on the side of a volcano is wiped out when the volcano erupts. |

Q3   The **isolation** of a group of animals can lead to **speciation**.

a)   Choose from the words provided to complete the definitions of isolation and speciation.

separated	species	joined	barrier

SPECIATION is when a new .... develops.

ISOLATION is where populations of a species are ....,

for example by a physical ....

b)   "Speciation can lead to extinction."
Tick the correct box to show whether this statement is **true** or **false**.

True ☐   **False** ☐

Extinction and Speciation

Q4 The diagrams below show the stages of **speciation**.
Draw lines to match the labels to the correct diagrams.

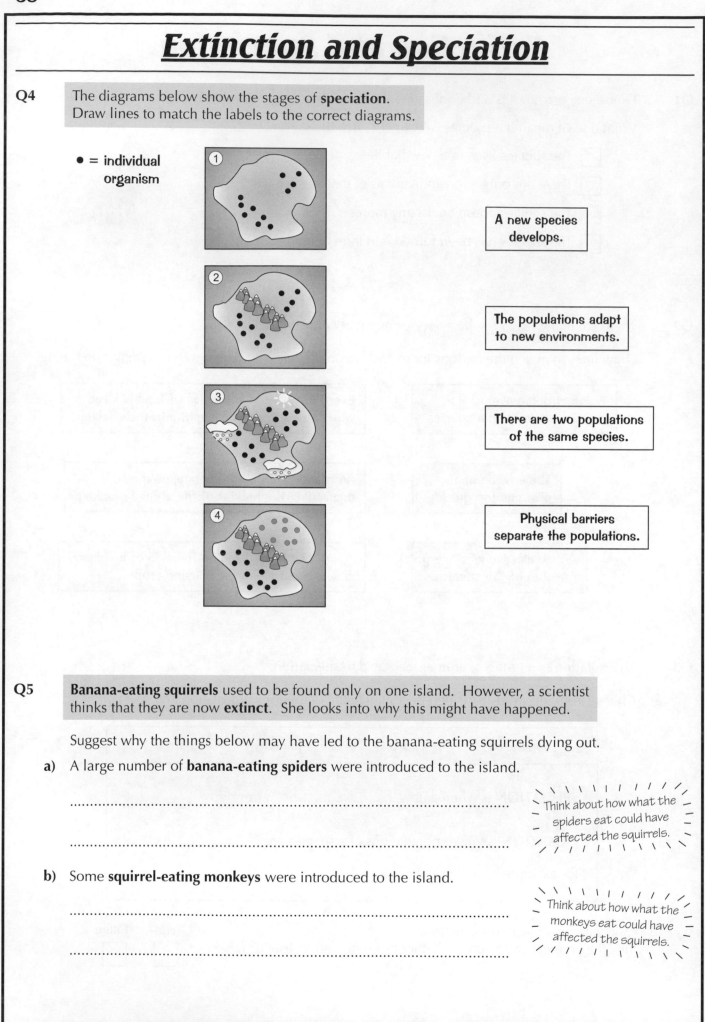

● = individual organism

A new species develops.

The populations adapt to new environments.

There are two populations of the same species.

Physical barriers separate the populations.

Q5 **Banana-eating squirrels** used to be found only on one island. However, a scientist thinks that they are now **extinct**. She looks into why this might have happened.

Suggest why the things below may have led to the banana-eating squirrels dying out.

a) A large number of **banana-eating spiders** were introduced to the island.

....

....

Think about how what the spiders eat could have affected the squirrels.

b) Some **squirrel-eating monkeys** were introduced to the island.

....

....

Think about how what the monkeys eat could have affected the squirrels.

Mixed Questions — Biology 2b

Q1   Your **sex** is determined by your 23rd pair of chromosomes — they're called **sex chromosomes**.

a)   Circle the correct words to complete these sentences about chromosomes.

   i)   A chromosome is a really **long** / **short** molecule of DNA.

   ii) Everyone (except identical twins) has **unique** / **identical** DNA in their chromosomes.

   iii) Every body cell contains **two** / **four** copies of each chromosome.

b)   Janice is **female**. What sex chromosomes does Janice have in her cells?

   ....

c)   Mark is **male**. What sex chromosomes does Mark have in his cells?

   ....

Q2   In one of **Gregor Mendel's** experiments, he crossed purple-flowered pea plants with white-flowered plants. The **genetic diagram** below shows one of Mendel's crosses. **C** represents the allele for **purple** flowers and **c** represents the allele for **white** flowers.

a)   Complete the genetic diagram.

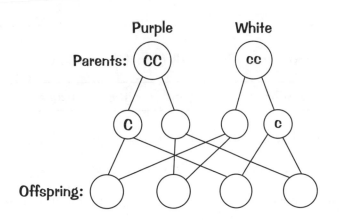

b)   In this experiment, which characteristic was **recessive**? Circle the correct answer.

   White flowers   **Purple flowers**

c)   In this cross, what is the probability of the offspring having white flowers? Circle the correct answer.

   100%   75%   50%   25%   0%

Mixed Questions — Biology 2b

Q3   Medical research is being done on **stem cells**.

a)   What can stem cells do that ordinary body cells can't?

....

b)   Scientists have experimented with growing stem cells in different conditions.

i)   What is the name of the process by which stem cells **divide** for growth?

mitosis   fertilisation   differentiation   meiosis

ii) Why are scientists interested in **embryonic** stem cells? Tick the right answer.

☐ They have the potential to turn into certain types of cell.

☐ They have the potential to turn into any kind of cell.

☐ They have the potential to turn into blood cells only.

c)   Do **animal cells** or **plant cells** lose the ability to differentiate at an early stage?

....

Q4   Neela runs a **100 m race**.

a)   Describe how Neela's heart rate **changed** when she was running.

....

b)   Complete the following passage using words from the list below.

anaerobic	aerobic	hydrogen	nitric	oxygen	fatigue	lactic

Neela was exercising hard, so she couldn't get enough .... to her muscles.

They started using .... respiration, which is respiration without oxygen.

This type of respiration makes .... acid in the muscles.

This acid causes muscle ...., which made Neela's legs feel tired.

c)   Neela was hungry after the race, so she ate a sandwich.

i)   Which enzyme breaks down the starch from the bread into sugars? Circle the correct answer.

lipase   protease   amylase

ii) Name **one** place in Neela's body where this enzyme is produced.

....

Biology 2b — Enzymes and Genetics

Mixed Questions — Biology 2b

Q5   The diagram shows a cliff and the places where three **fossils** were found in the cliff.

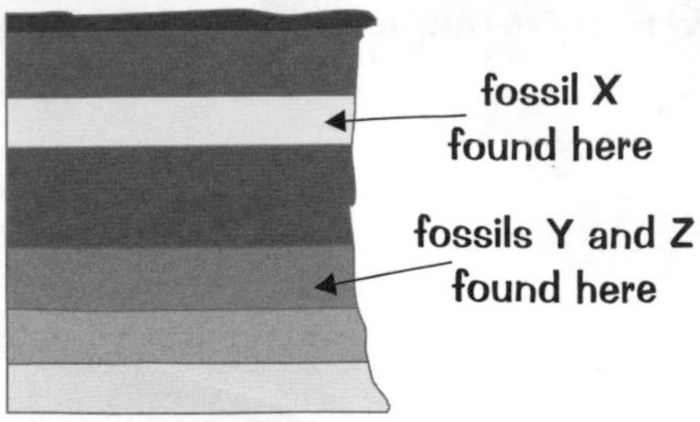

fossil **X** found here

fossils **Y** and **Z** found here

a)   Which of the three fossils marked on the diagram is most likely to be **most recent** fossil? Tick the correct answer.

X ☐   Y ☐   Z ☐

b)   Suggest **one** thing that scientists can learn from looking at fossils.

....

....

Q6   One way that organisms **grow** is by making new cells by **mitosis**.

This graph shows how the amount of DNA in a body cell changes as it goes through **mitosis**.

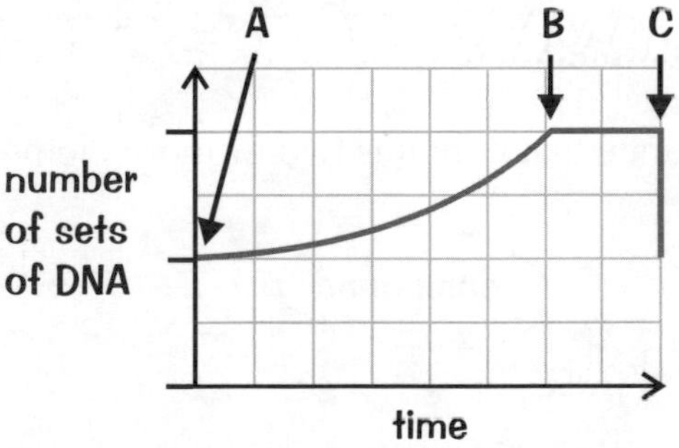

number of sets of DNA

time

a)   What is happening to the DNA in the cell between point A and point B? Circle the correct answer.

It is being copied.   It is being destroyed.   It is being moved around.

b)   At what point on the graph does the cell divide? Tick the correct answer.

A ☐   B ☐   C ☐

c)   What type of reproduction takes place using mitosis? Circle the correct answer.

sexual reproduction   asexual reproduction

d)   **Meiosis** is another way to make new cells. Give **one difference** between mitosis and meiosis.

....

....

Atoms, Compounds and Isotopes

Q1 **Complete** this table to show the relative masses of the particles in an atom.

Particle	Relative Mass
Proton	1
Neutron	1
Electron	0

Q2 Elements have a **mass number** and an **atomic number**.

a) Circle the **mass number** on the diagram to the right.

$^{12}_{6}\text{C}$ (12 circled)

b) What does the **mass number** of an element tell you?

The total number of protons and electrons

c) What is the name for a substance that contains two or more elements chemically combined? Circle your answer.

atom   (compound)   isotope

Q3 Choose the correct words from the list to **complete** this paragraph.

element	isotopes	protons	neutrons

Isotopes are atoms of the same element which have the same number of protons but a different number of neutrons.

Q4 a) Work out the number of **protons** and **neutrons** for each of these atoms.

W $^{12}_{6}\text{C}$ X $^{4}_{2}\text{He}$ Y $^{14}_{6}\text{C}$

protons 6   2   6

neutrons 6   2   8

b) Which two of the atoms are isotopes of each other? W and Y

Ionic Bonding

Q1   Tick the boxes to show whether the following statements are **true** or **false**.   **True False**

a)   In ionic bonding, atoms lose or gain electrons.   ☑ ☐

b)   Ions always have a positive charge.   ☐ ☑

c)   Ions with opposite charges attract each other.   ☑ ☐

d)   When atoms form ionic bonds they have the same
electronic structure as the noble gases.   ☑ ☐

e)   In ionic bonding, electrons from the inner shell are transferred.   ☐ ☑

f)   Ionic compounds can never conduct electricity.   ☐ ☑

Q2   Sodium (Na) and chlorine (Cl) react to form **sodium chloride**.

Look at the diagrams of the electronic structures of sodium and chlorine below.

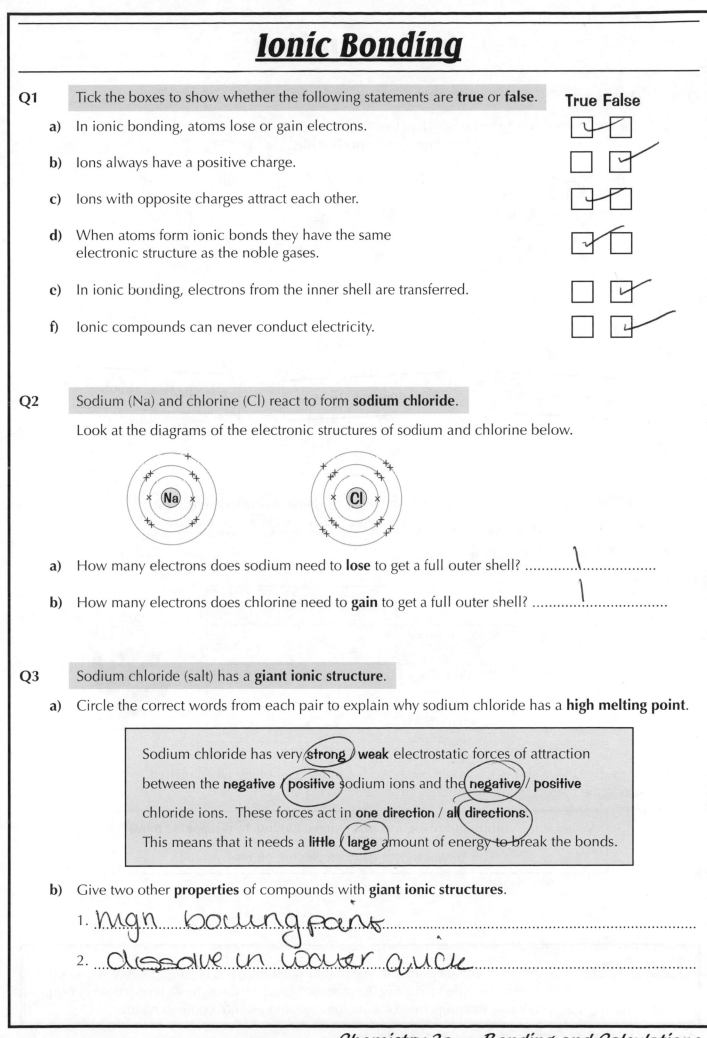

a)   How many electrons does sodium need to **lose** to get a full outer shell? ....1..................

b)   How many electrons does chlorine need to **gain** to get a full outer shell? ....1...................

Q3   Sodium chloride (salt) has a **giant ionic structure**.

a)   Circle the correct words from each pair to explain why sodium chloride has a **high melting point**.

> Sodium chloride has very (strong) / weak electrostatic forces of attraction
>
> between the **negative** /(positive) sodium ions and the (negative)/ positive
>
> chloride ions. These forces act in **one direction** /(all directions.)
>
> This means that it needs a **little** /(large) amount of energy to break the bonds.

b)   Give two other **properties** of compounds with **giant ionic structures**.

1. high boiling point

2. dissolve in water quick

Ionic Bonding

Q4   Diagrams can be used to show the **structures** of substances.

a)   Tick the correct box to show which of the diagrams below
could be used to show the bonding in **sodium chloride**.

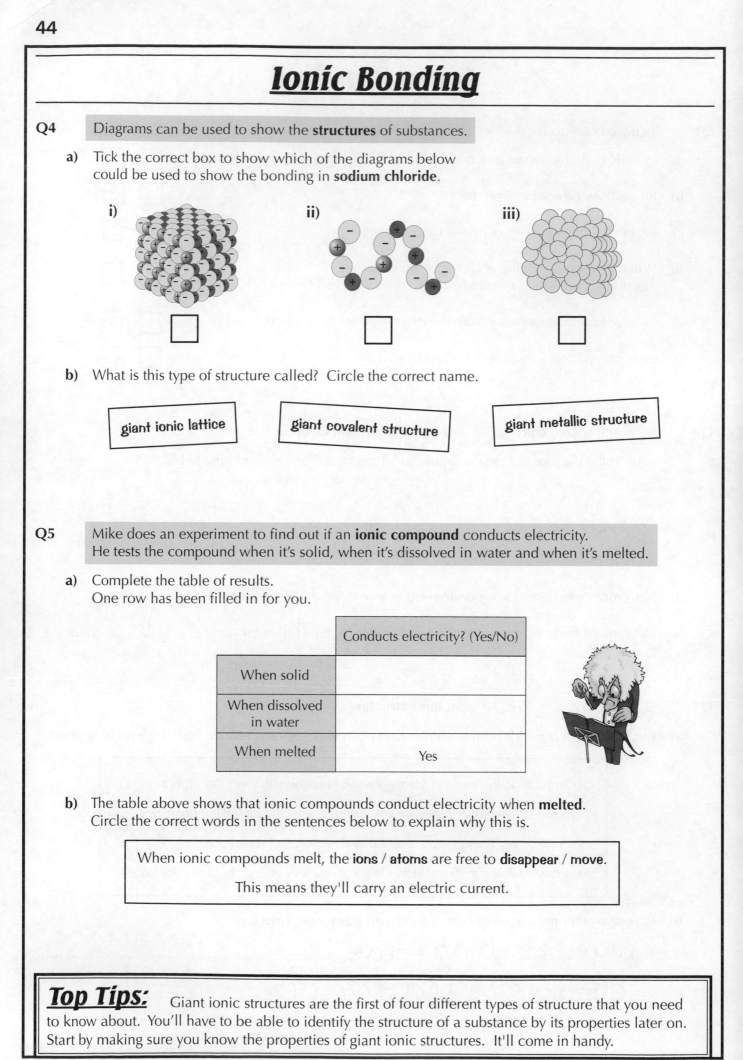

i)   ☐   ii)   ☐   iii)   ☐

b)   What is this type of structure called? Circle the correct name.

giant ionic lattice   giant covalent structure   giant metallic structure

Q5   Mike does an experiment to find out if an **ionic compound** conducts electricity.
He tests the compound when it's solid, when it's dissolved in water and when it's melted.

a)   Complete the table of results.
One row has been filled in for you.

	Conducts electricity? (Yes/No)
When solid	
When dissolved in water	
When melted	Yes

b)   The table above shows that ionic compounds conduct electricity when **melted**.
Circle the correct words in the sentences below to explain why this is.

When ionic compounds melt, the **ions** / **atoms** are free to **disappear** / **move**.

This means they'll carry an electric current.

Top Tips: Giant ionic structures are the first of four different types of structure that you need
to know about. You'll have to be able to identify the structure of a substance by its properties later on.
Start by making sure you know the properties of giant ionic structures. It'll come in handy.

Ions and Formulas

Q1 Use the **diagram** to help you answer the following questions.

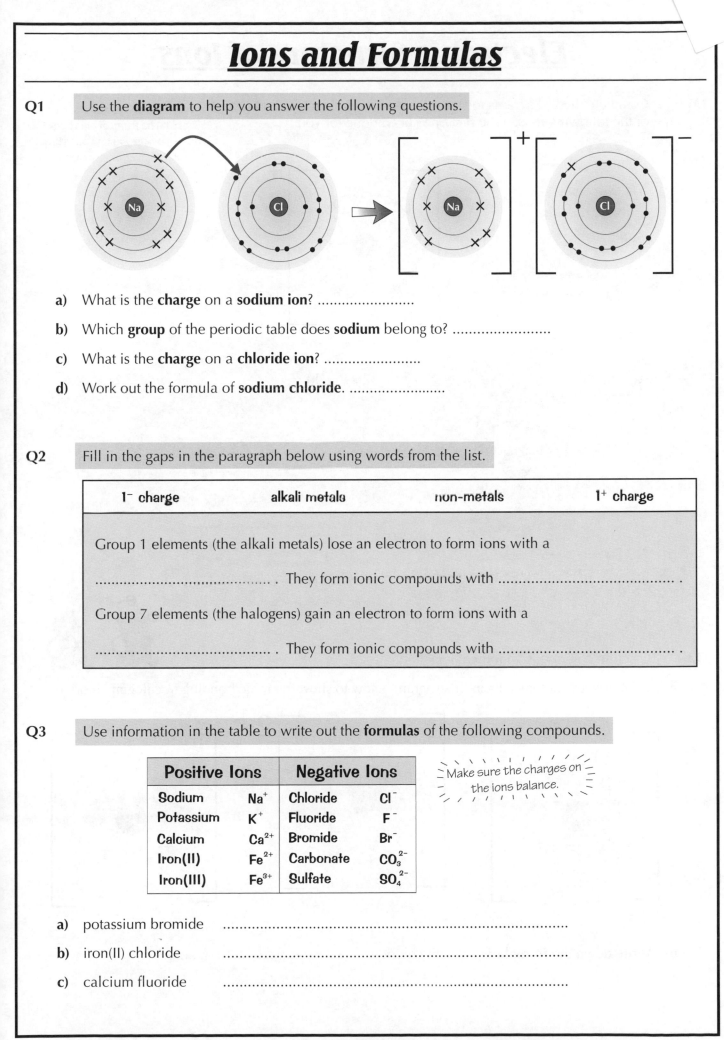

a) What is the **charge** on a **sodium ion**? ....

b) Which **group** of the periodic table does **sodium** belong to? ....

c) What is the **charge** on a **chloride ion**? ....

d) Work out the formula of **sodium chloride**. ....

Q2 Fill in the gaps in the paragraph below using words from the list.

1⁻ charge	alkali metals	non-metals	1⁺ charge

Group 1 elements (the alkali metals) lose an electron to form ions with a

.... They form ionic compounds with ....

Group 7 elements (the halogens) gain an electron to form ions with a

.... They form ionic compounds with ....

Q3 Use information in the table to write out the **formulas** of the following compounds.

Positive Ions		Negative Ions	
Sodium	Na^+	Chloride	Cl^-
Potassium	K^+	Fluoride	F^-
Calcium	Ca^{2+}	Bromide	Br^-
Iron(II)	Fe^{2+}	Carbonate	CO_3^{2-}
Iron(III)	Fe^{3+}	Sulfate	SO_4^{2-}

Make sure the charges on the ions balance.

a) potassium bromide ....

b) iron(II) chloride ....

c) calcium fluoride ....

Electronic Structure of Ions

Q1 Complete these diagrams to show the **electronic structure** and **charge** of the following **ions**. (The first one's been done for you.)

Use the periodic table in the front of this book to help you find out the number of electrons.

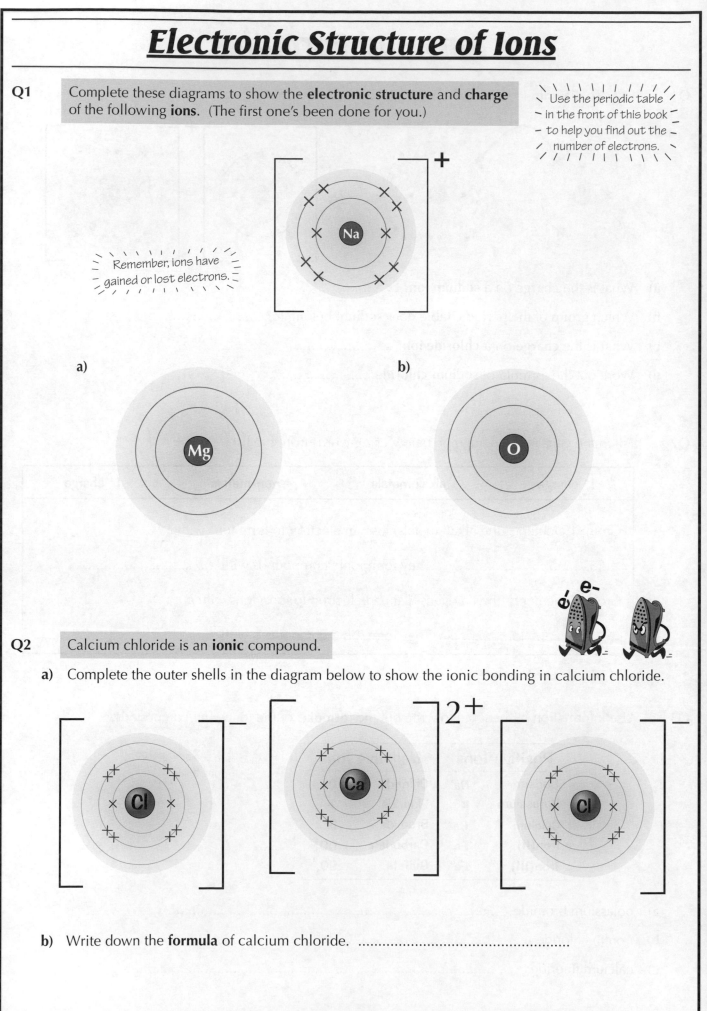

Remember, ions have gained or lost electrons.

a)

b)

Q2 Calcium chloride is an **ionic** compound.

a) Complete the outer shells in the diagram below to show the ionic bonding in calcium chloride.

b) Write down the **formula** of calcium chloride. ....

Covalent Bonding

Q1   Indicate whether each statement is **true** or **false**.

                                                                                 True False

     a)   Atoms make covalent bonds by sharing electrons.   ☐ ☐

     b)   Atoms make covalent bonds to get a full outer shell of electrons.   ☐ ☐

     c)   Hydrogen can form two covalent bonds.   ☐ ☐

     d)   Carbon can form four covalent bonds.   ☐ ☐

Q2   **Complete** the following table to show how many electrons are needed to **fill up** the **outer shell** of these atoms.

Atom	Carbon	Chlorine	Hydrogen	Nitrogen	Oxygen
Electronic Structure	2,4	2,8,7	1	2,5	2,6
Number of electrons needed to fill outer shell					

Q3   Complete the following diagrams by adding the **electrons**. Only the outer shells are shown.

     a)   Hydrogen chloride (HCl)   **b)**   Oxygen (O_2)

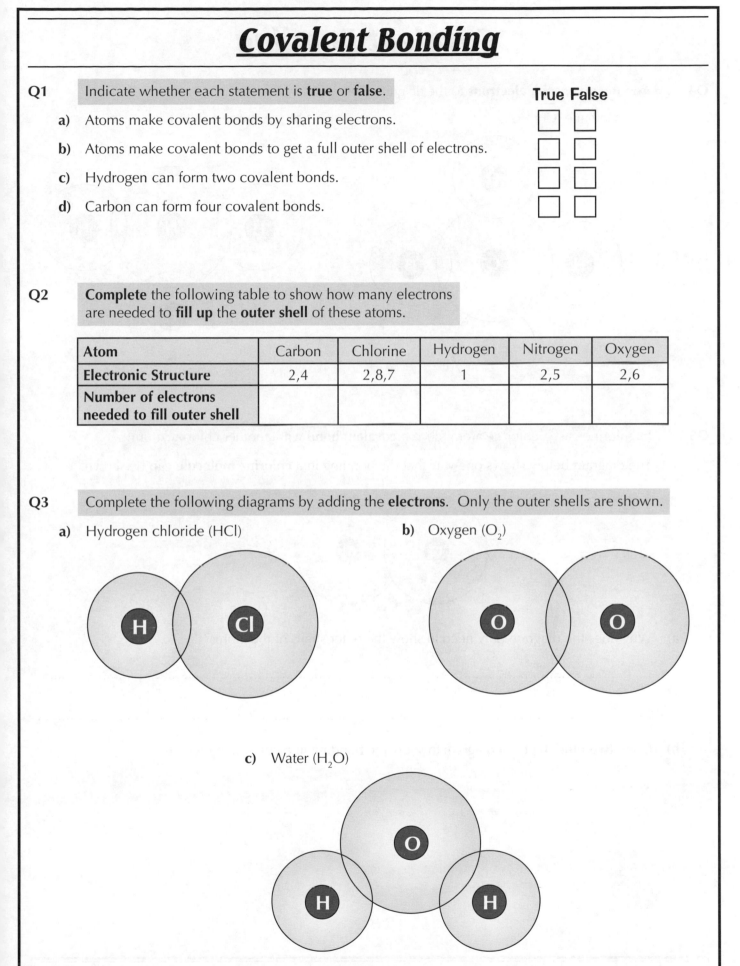

     c)   Water (H_2O)

Covalent Bonding

Q4 Add the outer shell **electrons** to the diagrams below.

a) Methane (CH$_4$) **b)** Ammonia (NH$_3$)

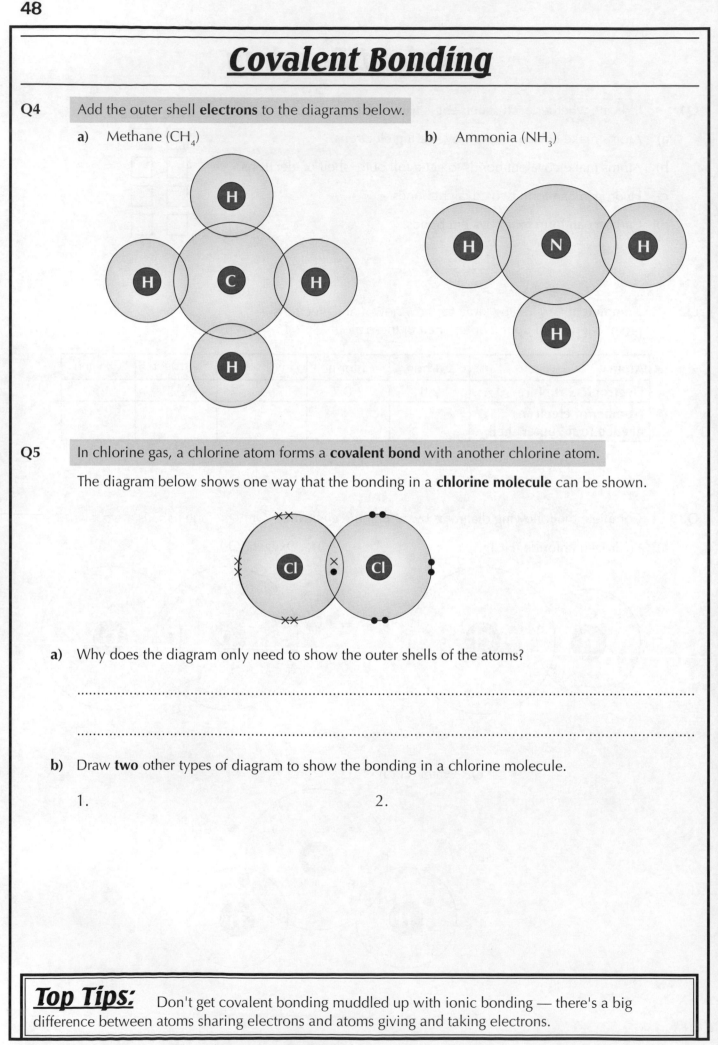

Q5 In chlorine gas, a chlorine atom forms a **covalent bond** with another chlorine atom.

The diagram below shows one way that the bonding in a **chlorine molecule** can be shown.

a) Why does the diagram only need to show the outer shells of the atoms?

....

....

b) Draw **two** other types of diagram to show the bonding in a chlorine molecule.

1.   2.

Top Tips: Don't get covalent bonding muddled up with ionic bonding — there's a big difference between atoms sharing electrons and atoms giving and taking electrons.

49

Covalent Substances — Two Kinds

Q1 Which am I — **diamond**, **graphite** or **silicon dioxide**?

Match up the sentences in the boxes to the drawings below.

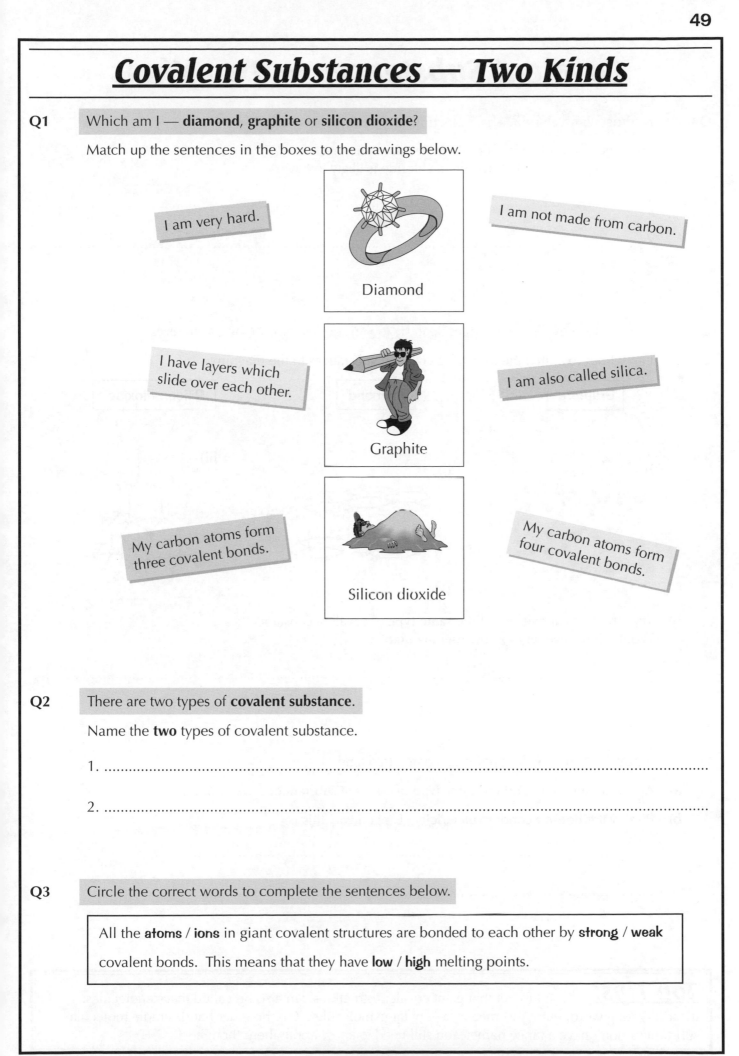

I am very hard.

I am not made from carbon.

Diamond

I have layers which slide over each other.

I am also called silica.

Graphite

My carbon atoms form three covalent bonds.

My carbon atoms form four covalent bonds.

Silicon dioxide

Q2 There are two types of **covalent substance**.

Name the **two** types of covalent substance.

1. ....

2. ....

Q3 Circle the correct words to complete the sentences below.

All the **atoms** / **ions** in giant covalent structures are bonded to each other by **strong** / **weak** covalent bonds. This means that they have **low** / **high** melting points.

Chemistry 2a — Bonding and Calculations

Covalent Substances — Two Kinds

Q4 Hydrogen and chlorine share electrons to form **hydrogen chloride**.

Hydrogen chloride has a **simple molecular** structure.
Give two properties that hydrogen chloride is likely to have.

1. ....

2. ....

Q5 You can tell covalent substances apart by looking at diagrams of their **structures**.

a) Draw lines to match the following **covalent substances** to the diagrams.

| Graphite | Diamond | Silicon dioxide |

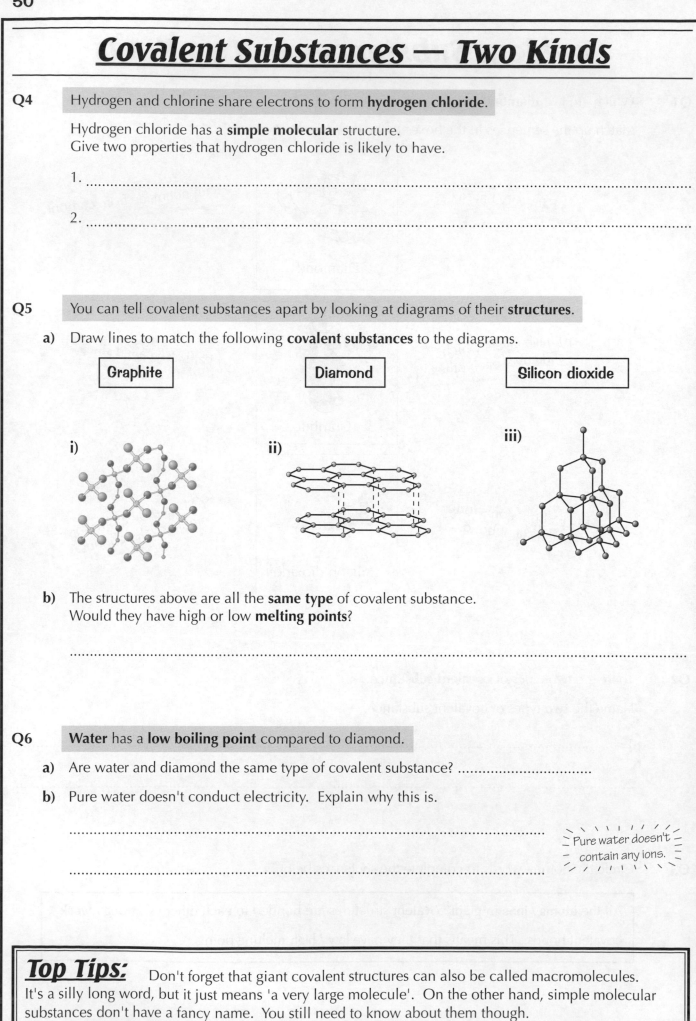

i)

ii)

iii)

b) The structures above are all the **same type** of covalent substance.
Would they have high or low **melting points**?

....

Q6 **Water** has a **low boiling point** compared to diamond.

a) Are water and diamond the same type of covalent substance? ....

b) Pure water doesn't conduct electricity. Explain why this is.

....

....

Pure water doesn't contain any ions.

Top Tips: Don't forget that giant covalent structures can also be called macromolecules. It's a silly long word, but it just means 'a very large molecule'. On the other hand, simple molecular substances don't have a fancy name. You still need to know about them though.

Metals and Identifying Structures

Q1 Metals have a **giant structure**.

Circle the correct word(s) from each pair in the passage below.

> Atoms in a metal are arranged in **a regular** / **an irregular** pattern.
>
> The layers of **atoms** / **molecules** in a metal can slide over each other.
>
> This means metals can be **snapped** / **bent**.

Q2 Copper is a **pure metal**. Brass is an **alloy**.

a) What is an alloy? Tick the box next to the correct answer.

An alloy doesn't contain any metal. ☐

An alloy is a pure metal. ☐

An alloy is a mixture of two or more metals. ☐

b) i) Which would you expect to be harder — brass or copper? ....

ii) Explain your answer.

....

....

....

....

Q3 Draw lines to match the type of **structure** to its properties.

Giant covalent	Don't conduct electricity when solid. Do conduct electricity when liquid.
Giant ionic	Have high melting points. Don't conduct electricity when melted.
Simple molecular	Have low melting points. Don't conduct electricity when melted.

Identifying Structures

Q1   Complete the following table by placing a **tick** or a **cross** in each box.   Two have been done for you.

Property	Giant Ionic	Giant Covalent	Simple Molecular
High melting and boiling points			
Can conduct electricity when solid		X	
Can conduct electricity when melted		X	

Q2   The **properties** of three substances are given below.

Substance	Melting Point (°C)	Good Electrical Conductor?
A	2000	Only when melted or dissolved
B	2500	No
C	20	No

Identify the **structure** of each substance. Use the words from the list below. Give a reason for each answer.

> giant covalent   giant ionic   simple molecular

Only use each option once.

a)   Substance A: ....

    Reason: ....

    ....

b)   Substance B: ....

    Reason: ....

    ....

c)   Substance C: ....

    Reason: ....

    ....

New Materials

Q1 **Nitinol** is a new material.

a) True or false?

   True False

i) Nitinol is a shape memory alloy.

ii) Light causes nitinol to change shape.

iii) When cool, nitinol can bend and twist.

iv) When heated, nitinol goes back to a 'remembered' shape.

b) Give one use of nitinol.

....

Q2 **Nanoparticles** are a new type of material.

a) Circle the correct words from each pair in the sentences below.

> Nanoparticles contain roughly a few **hundred** / **thousand** atoms.
>
> Nanoparticles have **identical** / **different** properties to the bulk chemical they are made from.
>
> Nanoparticles have a **huge** / **tiny** surface area compared to their volume.

b) The **properties** of nanoparticles determine their use. Draw lines to match the properties and uses.

Strong and light

Can detect one type of molecule and nothing else

Act like ball bearings to reduce friction

Lubricant coatings

Building materials

Sensors

c) What is the study of nanoparticles known as? Circle the correct word from the list below.

particle science   nanoscience   nanometres   shape memory alloys

Top Tips: The examiner might ask you to talk about the pros and cons of new materials. So, if you're wondering, the upside is the exciting new materials and their cool uses. The downside is that nanoparticles haven't been around for long so they might turn out to be harmful. Who knows?

Polymers

Q1 **Polymer** molecules are **long chains**, as shown in the diagrams.

A   **B**

a) Which diagram, A or B, shows a **thermosoftening** polymer? ....

b) **Thermosetting** polymers don't melt when heated. Why is this? Circle the correct answer.

They have crosslinks between the chains of polymers.

The chains of polymers are tangled.

Q2 Certain things affect the properties of **polymers**.

Tick the one thing from the list below that **doesn't** affect the properties of a polymer.

What the polymer is made from. ☐   **How much is made in the reaction.** ☐

The reaction conditions. ☐   **The catalyst used in the reaction.** ☐

Q3 **High density** (HD) **polythene** and **low density** (LD) **polythene** have different properties.

The table compares some of their properties.

	DENSITY	SOFTENING TEMPERATURE	FLEXIBILITY
LD	Low	Below 100 °C	High
HD	High	Above 100 °C	Fairly low

For each of the following uses choose which type of
polythene should be used. Give reasons for your choices.

When hospital equipment is sterilised it's heated to a high temperature.

a) hospital equipment that has to be sterilised ....

....

b) freezer bags ....

....

c) toothpaste tubes ....

....

Chemistry 2a — Bonding and Calculations

Relative Formula Mass

Q1   The **relative atomic mass** of an element can be found on the periodic table.

a)   The element helium is shown below as it is on the periodic table.
Circle its relative atomic mass.

$$\begin{array}{c} 4 \\ 2 \end{array} \text{He}$$

Use a periodic table to help you. There's one at the front of this book.

A, me hearties

b)   What are the **relative atomic masses (A$_r$)** of the following:

i)   sulfur (S) ....

iv) hydrogen (H) ....

vii)   potassium (K) ....

ii) nitrogen (N) ....

v) carbon (C) ....

viii)   calcium (Ca) ....

iii) oxygen (O) ....

vi) copper (Cu) ....

ix)   chlorine (Cl) ....

Q2 a)   Explain how the **relative formula mass** of a **compound** is calculated.

....

b)   What are the **relative formula masses (M$_r$)** of the following:

Use your answers to Q1 to help you.

i)   water (H$_2$O)

....

ii) potassium hydroxide (KOH)

....

iii) nitric acid (HNO$_3$)

....

iv) sulfuric acid (H$_2$SO$_4$)

....

v) copper sulfate (CuSO$_4$)

....

Top Tips:
The periodic table really comes in useful here. There's no way you'll be able to answer these questions without one (unless you've memorised all the elements' relative atomic masses — and that would just be silly). And lucky for you, you'll get given one in your exam. Yay!

Calculating Percentage Mass

Q1 a) There is a **formula** for calculating the **percentage mass** of an element in a compound.

Choose from the words below to complete the formula.

A_r No. of atoms (of that element) M_r (of whole compound)

$$\text{Percentage mass of an element in a compound} = \frac{\text{.......................} \times \text{.......................}}{\text{.......................}} \times 100$$

b) Ammonium nitrate, NH_4NO_3, contains nitrogen.

i) Use a periodic table to find the relative atomic mass of nitrogen.

....

ii) How many atoms of nitrogen are there in ammonium nitrate?

....

iii) Work out the relative formula mass of ammonium nitrate.

....

iv) Work out the percentage mass of nitrogen in ammonium nitrate.

....

Q2 a) Calculate the percentage mass of **oxygen** in each of the following compounds.

i) Fe_2O_3 **ii)** H_2O **iii)** $CaCO_3$

b) Which compound has the **greatest** percentage mass of oxygen? ....

Percentage Yield and Reversible Reactions

Q1 Chemists often calculate **percentage yield**.

a) Complete the following paragraph using the words provided.

percentage yield	yield	lower	expect

The amount of product you get from a reaction is known as the ....

Chemists can work out what yield they'd .... to get from a reaction.

But in real life the actual yield is always .... than this.

.... compares the amount of product chemists really get with

what they expected to get.

b) Percentage yield is always lower than 100%. There are lots of reasons for this.
Draw lines to match up the reasons to the explanations.

The reaction is reversible.

Some of the product may be lost when it's separated from the reaction mixture.

A liquid is filtered to remove a solid.

Some of the reactants are used up in other reactions. So there is less reactant to make the product you want.

Some of the products react together and turn back into the reactants.

Unexpected reactions take place.

Q2 COP Chemicals makes **substance X** using a process that has a percentage yield of just **20%**.

Some customers feel that COP Chemicals doesn't care about sustainable development. Complete the action plan below to show how COP chemicals can change this.

COP CHEMICALS SUSTAINABLE DEVELOPMENT ACTION PLAN:

1) Use as few reactants as we can.

2) ....

3) ....

Top Tips: Remember that a 100% yield simply doesn't happen in the big bad real world. Your yield will always be somewhere between 0 and 100%. It's your job to remember why.

Chemical Analysis and Instrumental Methods

Q1   John did a **paper chromatography** experiment on sweet colourings.

a)   Number the boxes 1 to 4 to put his method in order.

☐ Put the filter paper in a beaker with some solvent.

☐ Draw a line in pencil near the bottom of some filter paper. Put a spot of the coloured solution on it.

☐ Compare the results against the results from known dyes to identify the food colourings.

☐ Put the sweet in a cup with some solvent.

b)   Below on the left are the results John got for a blue sweet. Below on the right are the results for some known dyes.

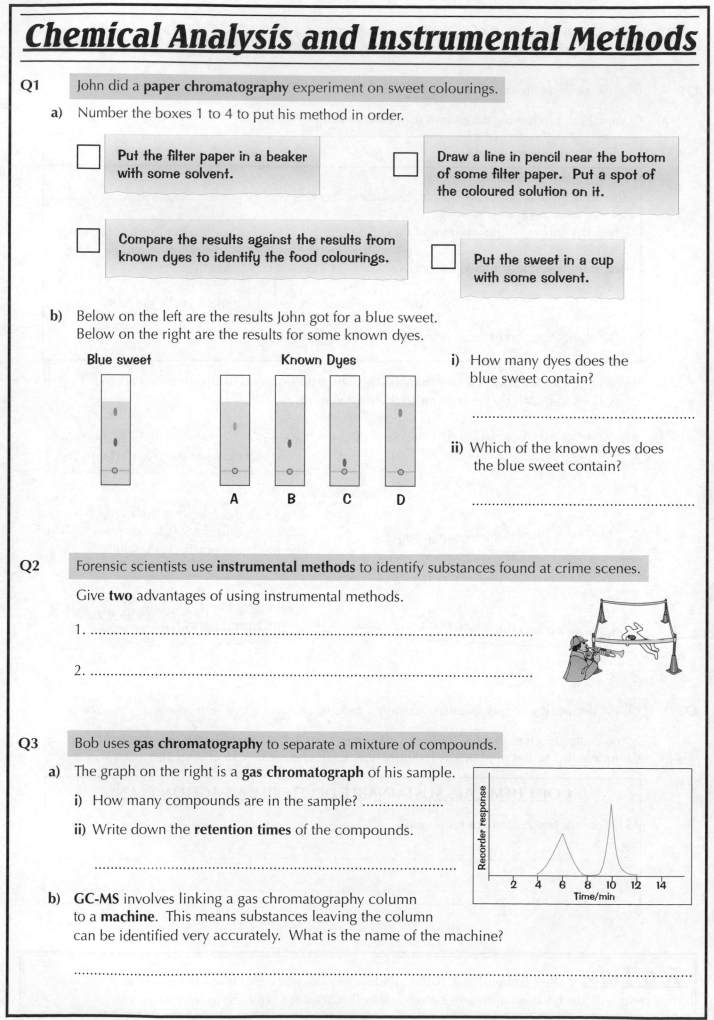

Blue sweet   **Known Dyes**

A   B   C   D

i) How many dyes does the blue sweet contain?

....

ii) Which of the known dyes does the blue sweet contain?

....

Q2   Forensic scientists use **instrumental methods** to identify substances found at crime scenes.

Give **two** advantages of using instrumental methods.

1. ....

2. ....

Q3   Bob uses **gas chromatography** to separate a mixture of compounds.

a)   The graph on the right is a **gas chromatograph** of his sample.

i) How many compounds are in the sample? ....

ii) Write down the **retention times** of the compounds.

....

b)   **GC-MS** involves linking a gas chromatography column to a **machine**. This means substances leaving the column can be identified very accurately. What is the name of the machine?

....

Mixed Questions — Chemistry 2a

Q1　Two forms of the element **carbon** are shown in the diagrams below.

R　　　　　　　　　　　　　　**S**

Key:
●　carbon atoms

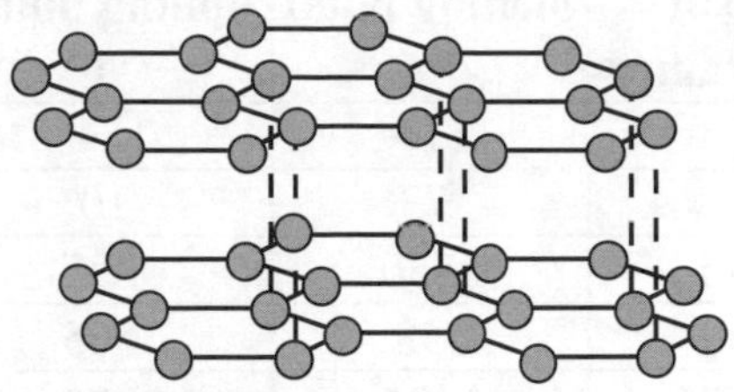

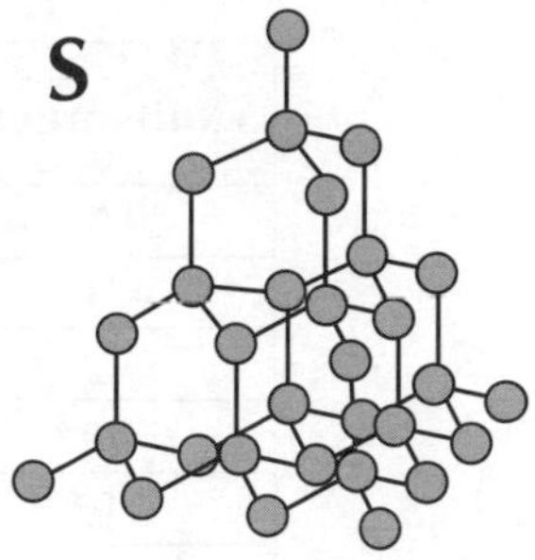

Tick the boxes to show whether the statements
about substances **R** and **S** are true or false.

True False

a)　R and S have the same type of bonding.　☐ ☐

b)　R and S are ionic substances.　☐ ☐

c)　Substance S could be silicon dioxide.　☐ ☐

d)　Substance R is graphite.　☐ ☐

e)　Both substances will have low melting points.　☐ ☐

Q2　Orwell found that silicon reacts with chlorine to produce **silicon chloride**, $SiCl_4$.

a)　Silicon chloride is a **simple molecular** substance.

　i) Would you expect silicon chloride to have a high boiling point or a low boiling point?

　...

　ii) Would silicon chloride conduct electricity?

　...

b)　**i)** Use a periodic table to find the **relative atomic mass** (A_r) of silicon and chlorine.

　　Silicon ....　　　　Chlorine ....

　ii) Work out the **relative formula mass** (M_r) of silicon chloride.

　...

c)　Calculate the **percentage mass** of chlorine in silicon chloride.

　...

　...

Mixed Questions — Chemistry 2a

Q3 The table gives the **properties** of some elements and compounds.

substance	state at room temp	melting point / °C	boiling point / °C	electrical conductivity	
				solid	liquid
A	solid	114	184	poor	poor
B	gas	-73	-10	poor	poor
C	solid	3550	4827	poor	poor
D	solid	858	1505	poor	good
E	solid	1495	2870	good	good
F	liquid	0	50	poor	poor

a) i) Identify one substance that is **likely** to have a **simple molecular** structure. ....

   ii) Explain your answer.

   ....

   ....

b) i) Which of the substances is **most likely** to have a **giant covalent** structure? ....

   ii) Explain your answer.

   ....

   ....

c) Substance **E** is a metal. It can be mixed with another metal to make an **alloy**.
   Tick the box below the diagram that shows the **structure** of an alloy.

   i) ☐

   ii) ☐

   iii) ☐

Q4 There are different types of **polymers**.

   Tick the boxes to show whether the following statements are true or false.

   True False

a) Thermosoftening polymers have crosslinks. ☐ ☐

b) Thermosetting polymers consist of individual tangled chains of polymers. ☐ ☐

c) Thermosetting polymers don't melted when heated. ☐ ☐

Mixed Questions — Chemistry 2a

Q5   Some reactions are **reversible**.

a)   Choose the correct word from each pair to complete the following sentence.

> A reversible reaction is one where the **products** / **catalysts** of the reaction
>
> can **escape** / **react** and turn back into **products** / **reactants**.

b)   Reversible reactions can affect the **percentage yield** of a reaction.

   i)   What is the **yield** of a reaction?

   ....

   ii)   What effect does a reaction being reversible have on the **percentage yield**?

   ....

Q6   Circle the correct word in each pair to complete the passage.

Ionic compounds have a **giant** / **simple** ionic lattice structure.

The oppositely charged **ions** / **atoms** in the compound are attracted to each other.

The forces of attraction are called **electrostatic** / **ionic** forces.

Q7   **Gas chromatography** is a type of instrumental analysis.

a)   Use the words below to fill in the gaps in this paragraph about gas chromatography.

| retention time | gas | identify | speeds | chromatograph | compounds | mass spectrometer |

A .... is used to carry substances through a column packed with a solid.

The substances travel through it at different ...., so they're separated.

The recorder draws a gas .... The number of peaks shows the number of

different .... in the sample. The position of the peaks shows the

.... of the substances. This helps to .... the substances.

The gas chromatography column can also be linked to a ....

b)   Some substances can also be identified using paper chromatography.
Give an **advantage** of using **gas chromatography** instead.

....

Rate of Reaction

Q1 The four statements below are about **rate of reaction**.
Circle the correct words from each pair to complete the sentences.

a) The **higher** / **lower** the temperature the faster the reaction.

b) A **higher** / **lower** concentration will reduce the rate of reaction.

c) A smaller surface area **increases** / **decreases** the rate of reaction.

d) A catalyst **does** / **doesn't** change the rate of reaction.

Q2 In an experiment, **different sizes** of marble chips were reacted with hydrochloric acid.
The **same mass** of marble was used each time. The graph below shows how much **gas**
was given off with large marble chips, medium marble chips and small marble chips.

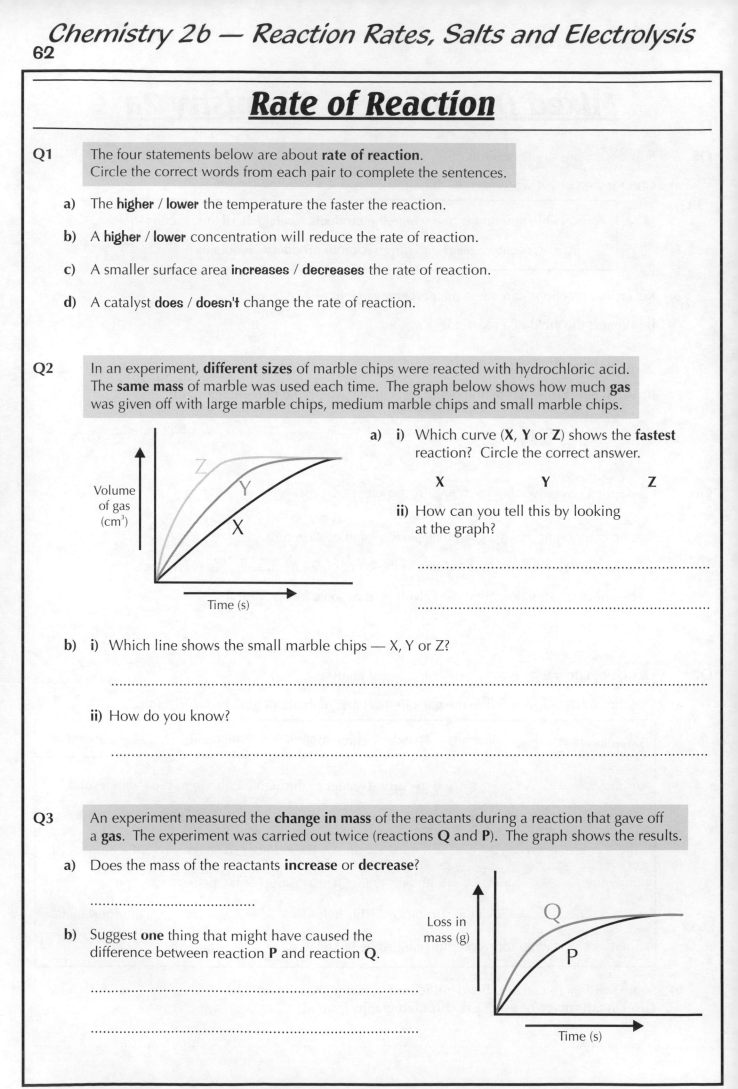

a) i) Which curve (**X**, **Y** or **Z**) shows the **fastest**
reaction? Circle the correct answer.

X   **Y**   **Z**

ii) How can you tell this by looking
at the graph?

....

....

b) i) Which line shows the small marble chips — X, Y or Z?

....

ii) How do you know?

....

Q3 An experiment measured the **change in mass** of the reactants during a reaction that gave off
a **gas**. The experiment was carried out twice (reactions **Q** and **P**). The graph shows the results.

a) Does the mass of the reactants **increase** or **decrease**?

....

b) Suggest **one** thing that might have caused the
difference between reaction **P** and reaction **Q**.

....

....

Measuring Rates of Reaction

Q1   Use the words provided to complete the sentences below about measuring rates of reaction.

faster	rate	volume	reactants	gas	mass	formed	precipitation

The .... of a reaction can be measured by observing either how quickly

the .... are used up or how quickly the products are ....

In a .... reaction you usually measure how quickly the product is formed.

The product turns the solution cloudy. The .... it turns cloudy the quicker

the reaction.

In a reaction that produces a .... you can measure how quickly the

.... of the reactants changes. You can also measure the

.... of gas given off in a set time using a gas syringe.

Q2   Sam reacted some marble chips with **different concentrations** of hydrochloric acid.
He kept the mass of marble and the volume of acid the same each time.
He measured the **loss in mass** of the reactants. Below is a graph of the results.

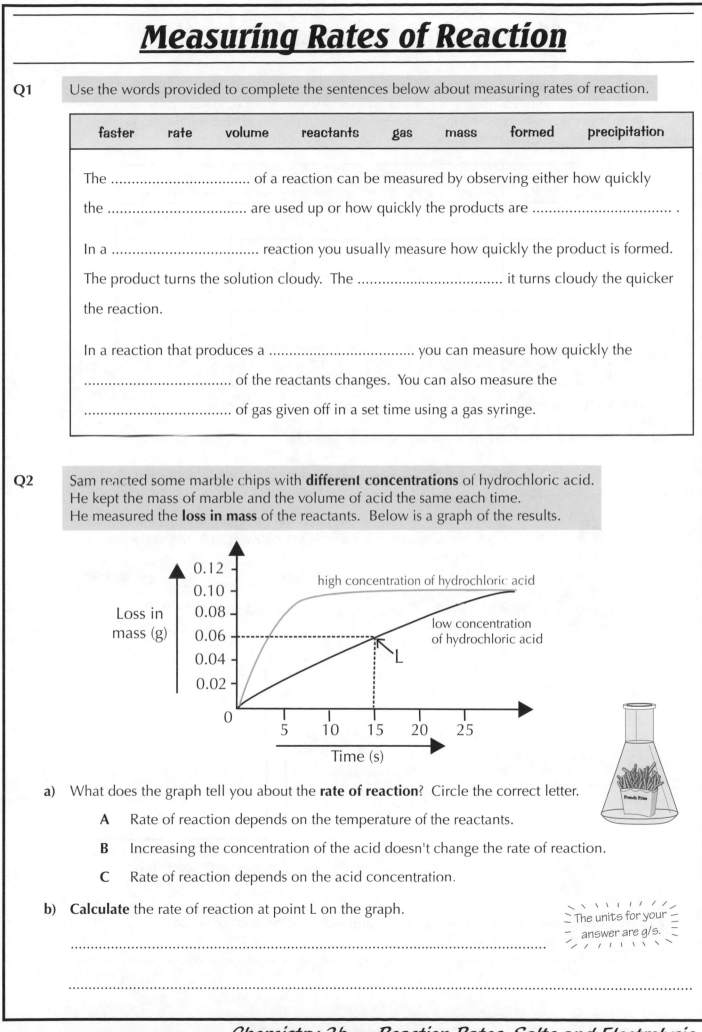

a)   What does the graph tell you about the **rate of reaction**? Circle the correct letter.

   A   Rate of reaction depends on the temperature of the reactants.

   B   Increasing the concentration of the acid doesn't change the rate of reaction.

   C   Rate of reaction depends on the acid concentration.

b)   **Calculate** the rate of reaction at point L on the graph.

The units for your answer are g/s.

....

....

Measuring Rates of Reaction

Q3   Charlie was comparing the rate of reaction of 5 g of magnesium ribbon with 20 ml of **five different concentrations** of hydrochloric acid (HCl). Each time he measured how much **gas** was produced during the **first minute** of the reaction. He did the experiment **twice** for each concentration of acid. These are his results:

Concentration of HCl (mol/dm³)	Experiment 1 — volume of gas given off (cm³)	Experiment 2 — volume of gas given off (cm³)	Average volume of gas given off (cm³)
2	92	96	$\frac{(92 + 96)}{2} = 94$
1.5	63	65	
1	44	47	
0.5	20	23	
0.25	9	9	

a)   **Fill in** the last column of the table. The first one has been done for you.

b)   Which concentration of hydrochloric acid produced the fastest rate of reaction? ....

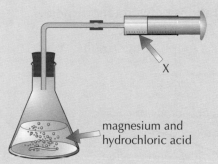

magnesium and hydrochloric acid

c)   A diagram of the **equipment** used in the experiment is shown on the left.

What is the name of the object labelled **X**? Circle your answer from the list below.

gas tube   gas syringe

delivery tube

d)   **Sketch** a graph of the average volume of gas given off against concentration of HCl.

You only need to plot the values very roughly. Just draw what the graph would look like.

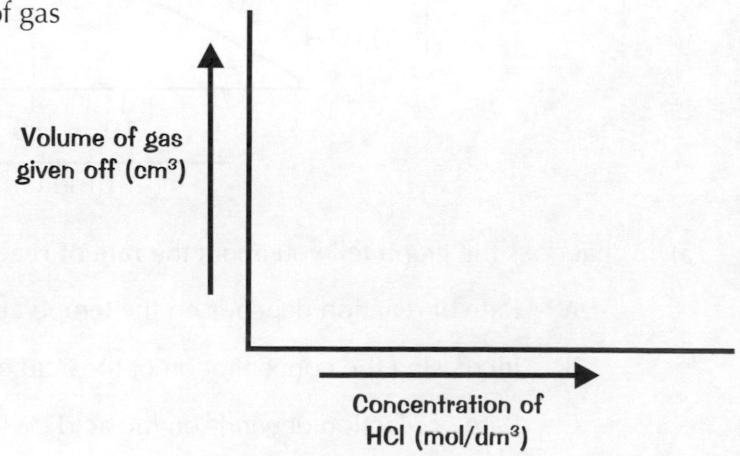

Volume of gas given off (cm³)

Concentration of HCl (mol/dm³)

e)   Why did Charlie do the experiment twice and work out the average volume?

....

Rate of Reaction Experiments

Q1   Choose from the words below to complete the paragraph.

sooner	larger	steeper	faster

Using smaller bits of a solid gives it a .... surface area.

This means it reacts .... This will give a ....

graph with the reaction finishing ....

Q2   Matilda did an experiment to find out the effect of **surface area** on rate of reaction.
She added dilute hydrochloric acid to **large marble chips** and measured the volume of gas given
off at regular times. She repeated the experiment using the same mass of **powdered marble**.
Below is a graph of her results.

a)   Which curve, A or B, did
Matilda get when she used
large chips of marble?

....

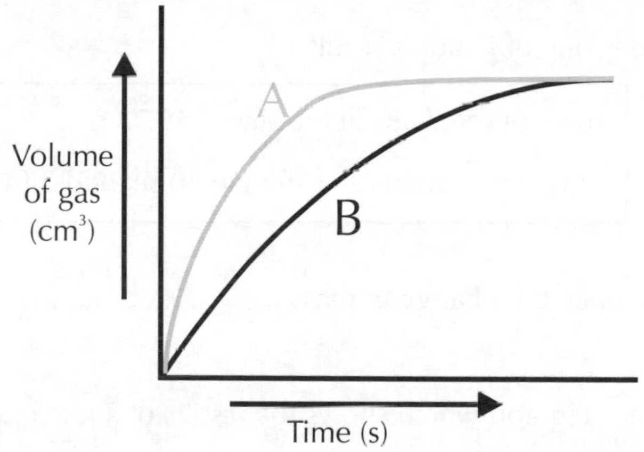

b)   On the graph opposite, draw
the curve you would get if you
used the **same mass** of **medium**
sized marble pieces. Label it C.

Volume
of gas
(cm^3)

A

B

Time (s)

c)   Name the **independent** variable in this investigation.

....

The independent variable is the thing you change.

d)   Is there enough information given above for you to be sure whether this was a **fair test** or not?
Tick the box next to the correct answer.

Yes, because the same mass of marble chips was used each time. ☐

No, because it is not known if the same volume of acid was
used each time or if the temperature was kept the same. ☐

e)   Which other method could you use to measure the rate of this reaction?
Tick the correct one.

☐ Timing how long the reaction takes to go cloudy.

☐ Timing how long the reaction takes to start.

☐ Measuring how quickly the reaction loses mass.

Rate of Reaction Experiments

Q3 Dillon investigated the reaction between **magnesium** and **hydrochloric acid**. He did the experiment using **different concentrations** of acid. He recorded the mass of the reactants at the start and at every 10 seconds for 2 minutes and calculated the change in mass for each reading.

a) Dillon is going to draw a graph of his results.
Match the labels to the axes for him.

loss in mass (g)	time (s)
x-axis	
y-axis	

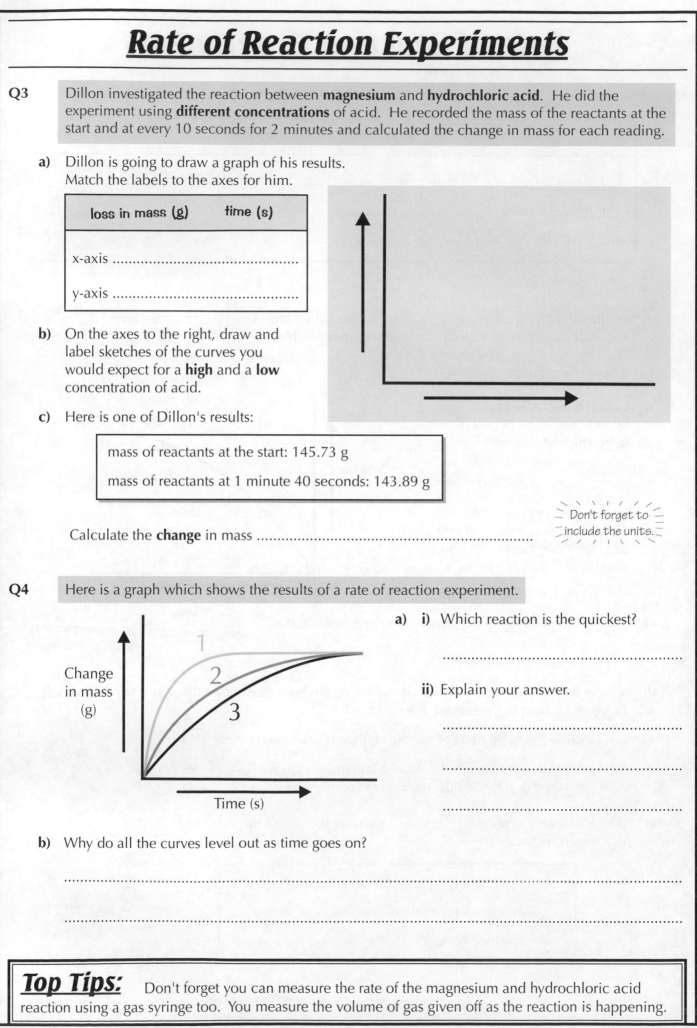

b) On the axes to the right, draw and label sketches of the curves you would expect for a **high** and a **low** concentration of acid.

c) Here is one of Dillon's results:

mass of reactants at the start: 145.73 g

mass of reactants at 1 minute 40 seconds: 143.89 g

Calculate the **change** in mass ....

Don't forget to include the units.

Q4 Here is a graph which shows the results of a rate of reaction experiment.

a) i) Which reaction is the quickest?

....

ii) Explain your answer.

....

....

....

b) Why do all the curves level out as time goes on?

....

....

Top Tips: Don't forget you can measure the rate of the magnesium and hydrochloric acid reaction using a gas syringe too. You measure the volume of gas given off as the reaction is happening.

Chemistry 2b — Reaction Rates, Salts and Electrolysis

Rate of Reaction Experiments

Q5 When you mix **sodium thiosulfate** solution and **hydrochloric acid**, a precipitate is formed. Circle the correct words to complete the statements about the reaction.

A precipitate is a **solid** / **liquid** that forms in a **solution** / **solid**.

The mixture goes **cloudy** / **clear**.

Q6 Yasmin investigates the effect of **temperature** on the rate of the reaction between sodium thiosulfate solution and hydrochloric acid. She mixes the reactants together in a flask. Then she times how long a cross placed under the flask takes to disappear.

a) Circle the items from the following list that she would need.

| scales | syringe | stopclock | thermometer |

b) Here are some results from her investigation:

Temperature (°C)	20	30	40	50	60
Time taken for cross to disappear (s)	201	177		112	82

i) As the temperature increases, does the reaction get **faster** or **slower**? ....

ii) One of the values in the table is missing. Circle the most likely value for it from the list below.

145 s   **192 s**   **115 s**

c) What could Yasmin do to make her results more **reliable**? Tick the correct box.

☐ Repeat the investigation to get more results. Then find the average for each temperature.

☐ Use a larger volume of hydrochloric acid in the experiment to make sure the reaction works well.

Q7 Nir reacts together sodium thiosulfate and hydrochloric acid. He looks at the effect of changing the **concentration** of hydrochloric acid on the rate of reaction. He mixes the reactants together in a flask. Then he times how long it takes for a cross placed under the flask to disappear.

He gets these results:

Concentration of acid (mol/dm^3)	2.00	1.75	1.50	1.25	1.00
Time taken for cross to disappear (s)	13	23	38	50	67

What can Nir tell about the effect of **concentration** on reaction rate from these results?

....

Rate of Reaction Experiments

Q8   Hydrogen peroxide **decomposes** (breaks down) and gives off oxygen.

a)   What is a good way to measure the rate of this reaction?
Circle the letter next to the correct answer.

    A   Weigh the amount of oxygen produced

    B   Time how long the reaction takes to go cloudy

    C   Measure the volume of gas produced at regular time intervals

    D   Measure the temperature

b)   Circle the correct word from the pair to complete the sentence.

> We can **increase** / **decrease** the speed of this reaction by using a catalyst.

Q9   Jim carried out an experiment to look at the effect of a **catalyst** on the rate of reaction.
He compared three different catalysts to see which was the most effective (increased
the rate of reaction the most). He used a gas syringe to measure the amount of gas
produced in the reaction. Below is a graph of his results.

a)   Which of the following labels
could be used on the y-axis?
Circle your answer.

   Volume of gas given off (g)

   Change in mass (g)

   Volume of gas given off (cm³)

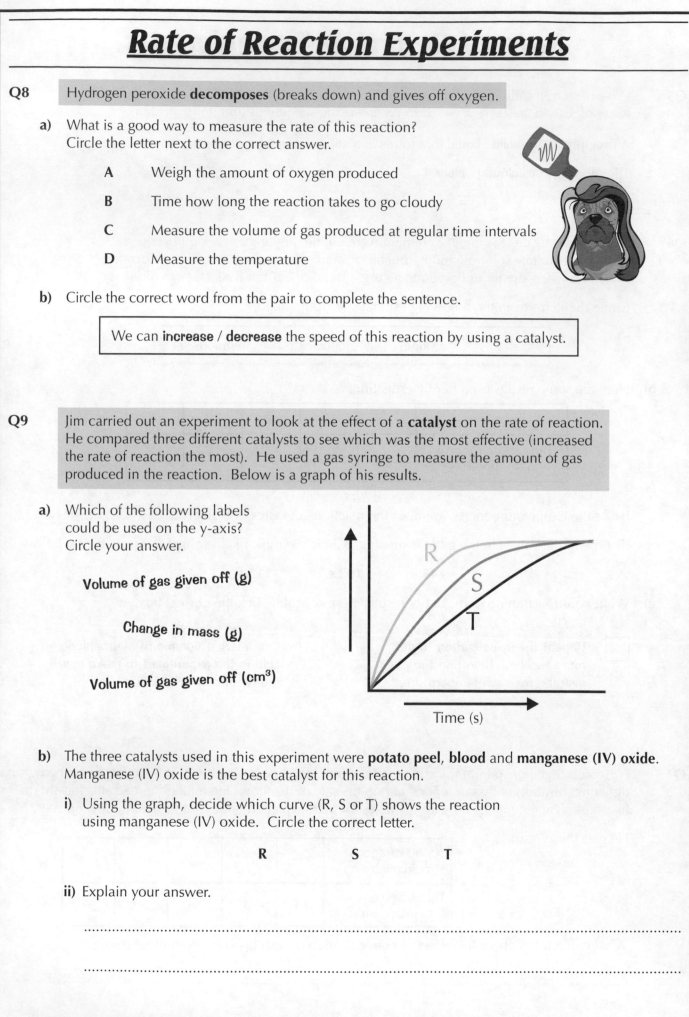

Time (s)

b)   The three catalysts used in this experiment were **potato peel**, **blood** and **manganese (IV) oxide**.
Manganese (IV) oxide is the best catalyst for this reaction.

   i) Using the graph, decide which curve (R, S or T) shows the reaction
   using manganese (IV) oxide. Circle the correct letter.

                    R   **S**   **T**

   ii) Explain your answer.

   ....

   ....

Collisions

Q1 Choose from the words below to fill in the gaps in the paragraph about collisions.

hard	faster	often	collisions

The rate of reaction can be explained by the .... between particles.

I low .... and how .... they collide affects

the rate of reaction. More and harder collisions means a .... rate.

Q2 Draw lines to match up the changes with their effects.

increasing the temperature

increasing the concentration

increasing the surface area

means there are more particles of reactant, so the particles collide more often

gives particles a bigger area of solid reactant to hit so they collide more often

makes the particles move faster, so they collide more often

Q3 Gases are always under **pressure**.

a) The diagrams below show gases at different pressures.
Draw lines to match the correct labels to the boxes.

high pressure

low pressure

b) i) If you increase the pressure of a gas reaction, does the rate **increase** or **decrease**?

....

ii) Explain your answer.

....

....

Collisions and Catalysts

Q1 Tick the boxes below to show whether the following statements are true or false.

True False

a) Higher temperature makes the particles move slower. ☐ ☐

b) Higher temperature increases the energy of the collisions. ☐ ☐

c) It doesn't matter how much energy particles collide with — the reaction will always happen. ☐ ☐

d) The smallest amount of energy particles need to react is known as the activation energy. ☐ ☐

e) All reactions can use the same catalyst. ☐ ☐

Q2 **Catalysts** are often used in reactions.

a) What is a catalyst? Circle the correct words in the sentence below.

> A catalyst is a substance which **speeds up** / **slows down** a reaction.
>
> Catalysts **are** / **aren't** used up in the reaction.

b) The diagram below shows the same reaction being carried out with a catalyst and without a catalyst.

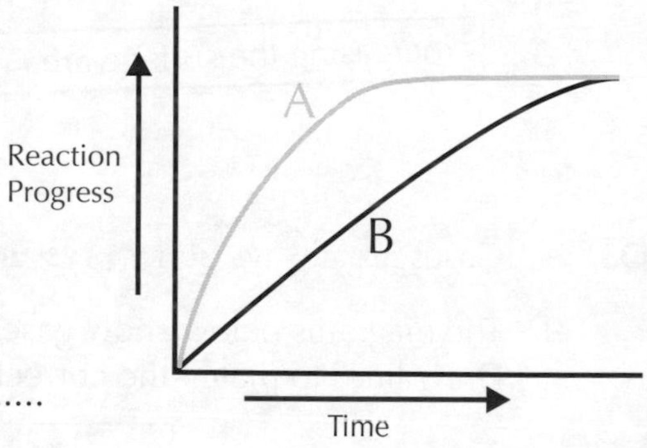

i) Which line shows the reaction with a catalyst, A or B?

....

ii) Explain your answer.

....

....

Reaction Progress / Time (A, B)

Q3 Catalysts are used in many **industrial reactions**.

a) Give **one** reason why catalysts are **useful** for industrial processes.

....

....

b) Give **one** possible **problem** with using catalysts in industrial processes.

....

Top Tips: Unlike other exciting things, such as chocolate buttons and a fashion for sparkly leggings, a catalyst isn't used up or changed. So you can use it again and again... and again.

Chemistry 2b — Reaction Rates, Salts and Electrolysis

Energy Transfer in Reactions

Q1 Circle the correct words from each pair in this paragraph about **exothermic** reactions.

> Exothermic reactions **give out** / **take in** energy **from** / **to** the surroundings.
>
> This is often shown by a **fall** / **rise** in **temperature** / **mass**.

Q2 Many reactions are **exothermic**.

Give three types of reaction that are exothermic.

1. ....

2. ....

3. ....

Q3 Use the words below to fill in the gaps in this paragraph about **endothermic** reactions.

heat	fall	take in
Endothermic reactions .... energy from the surroundings. They take in .... This causes a .... in temperature.		

Q4 When you heat limestone it breaks down to form quicklime and carbon dioxide.

a) The reaction requires a large amount of heat.

    i) Is it **exothermic** or **endothermic**? ....

    ii) Explain your answer.

....

b) Breaking down 1000 kg of limestone takes about 1 800 000 kJ of heat energy.

    i) How much heat energy would be needed to make **1 kg** of limestone break down?

....

    ii) How much limestone could be broken down by **900 000 kJ** of heat energy?

....

Chemistry 2b — Reaction Rates, Salts and Electrolysis

Energy Transfer in Reactions

Q5 Sam did an experiment to investigate the **thermal decomposition** of **copper sulfate**. He wrote this about his investigation:

"When I heated up blue copper sulfate it steamed and went white. After it cooled down I dropped a little water on it and it got really hot and turned blue again".

Water vapour

Answer these questions about Sam's observations:

a) Which part of Sam's experiment was exothermic? ....

b) Which part of Sam's experiment was endothermic? ....

c) Is blue copper sulfate **anhydrous** or **hydrated**? Circle the correct answer.

anhydrous

hydrated

Anhydrous means without water.
Hydrated means containing water.

d) Write a **word equation** for this reaction in the box using the words below.

anhydrous copper sulfate	water	hydrated copper sulfate
...., ...	....	$\rightleftharpoons$ + ...

e) What is a reaction that can go both ways called?

....

Q6 Here are some everyday uses of chemical reactions. Decide whether each reaction is endothermic or exothermic. In the box, put **N** for endothermic and **X** for exothermic.

a) Special cool packs are used by athletes to treat injuries. They take heat in and the pack becomes very cold. ☐

b) Self-heating cans of coffee contain chemicals in the base. When the chemicals are combined they produce heat which warms the can. ☐

c) Baking powder is used to make cakes rise. When it's heated in the oven it thermally decomposes to produce a gas. ☐

Top Tips: Anything that takes heat in is endothermic. Endothermic reactions are pretty rare in everyday life but you do get them. Think about cooking eggs or even melting ice cream in your mouth.

Acids and Alkalis

Q1 a) Complete the equation below for the reaction between an acid and a base.

acid + base → .... + ...

b) Circle the correct word that describes this kind of reaction.

decomposition   oxidation   neutralisation

c) Which of the following ions:

| hydrogen ions   hydroxide ions |

i) is present in an acidic solution? ....

ii) is present in an alkaline solution? ....

iii) would be present in a solution with a pH of 10? ....

iv) would be present in a solution with a pH of 2? ....

Q2 Choose from the words below to complete the following sentences.

pH   alkali   neutral   scale   7

a) Solutions which are not acidic or alkaline are said to be ....

b) An indicator can tell you the .... of a solution.

c) If a substance is neutral it has a pH of ....

d) A base that dissolves in water is known as an ....

e) The pH .... is a measure of how acidic or alkaline a solution is.

Q3 Joey wants to make **sodium chloride** (a salt). He adds hydrochloric acid to sodium hydroxide solution until the solution is neutral.

a) Complete this equation to show the reaction between hydrogen ions and hydroxide ions in this reaction.

Don't forget the state symbol.

$H^+_{(aq)}$ + $OH^-_{(aq)}$ → .... (.........)

b) Suggest what Joey could use to tell whether the reaction was **over**.

....

c) What would the pH of the products be? Circle your answer.

pH 14   pH 7   pH 6   pH 1

Acids and Alkalis

Q4 State symbols give the **physical state** of a substance.

Give the **symbols** for the following states.

a) Solid ☐

b) Liquid ☐

c) Gas ☐

d) Dissolved in water ☐

Q5 Ant stings hurt because of the **acid** they release.

The table on the right shows the pH values of some household substances.

Substance	pH
lemon juice	2
baking soda	9
vinegar	3

a) Suggest a substance from the list that could be used to make an ant sting feel better.

....

b) Explain your answer.

....

....

Q6 **Indigestion tablets** contain **bases** to neutralise extra stomach acid.

Joey wanted to test how well they work. He added a tablet to some hydrochloric acid, stirred it until it dissolved and tested the pH of the solution. He then dissolved a second, third and fourth tablet and tested the pH after each one. His results are shown in the table below.

Number of Tablets	pH
0	1
1	2
2	3
3	7
4	9

a) Plot a graph of the results.

b) Describe how the pH changes when the tablets are added to the acid.

....

c) How many tablets were needed to neutralise the acid? ....

Top Tips: State symbols might not look important but they tell you a lot about a reaction. You need to know if your products are going to be liquids or gases so you know how to collect them. For example, a gas will need a flask with a bung to stop it floating off around the room.

Chemistry 2b — Reaction Rates, Salts and Electrolysis

Acids Reacting With Metals

Q1   The diagram below shows **aluminium** reacting with **sulfuric acid**.

a)   Label the diagram using the names of the chemicals in the box below.

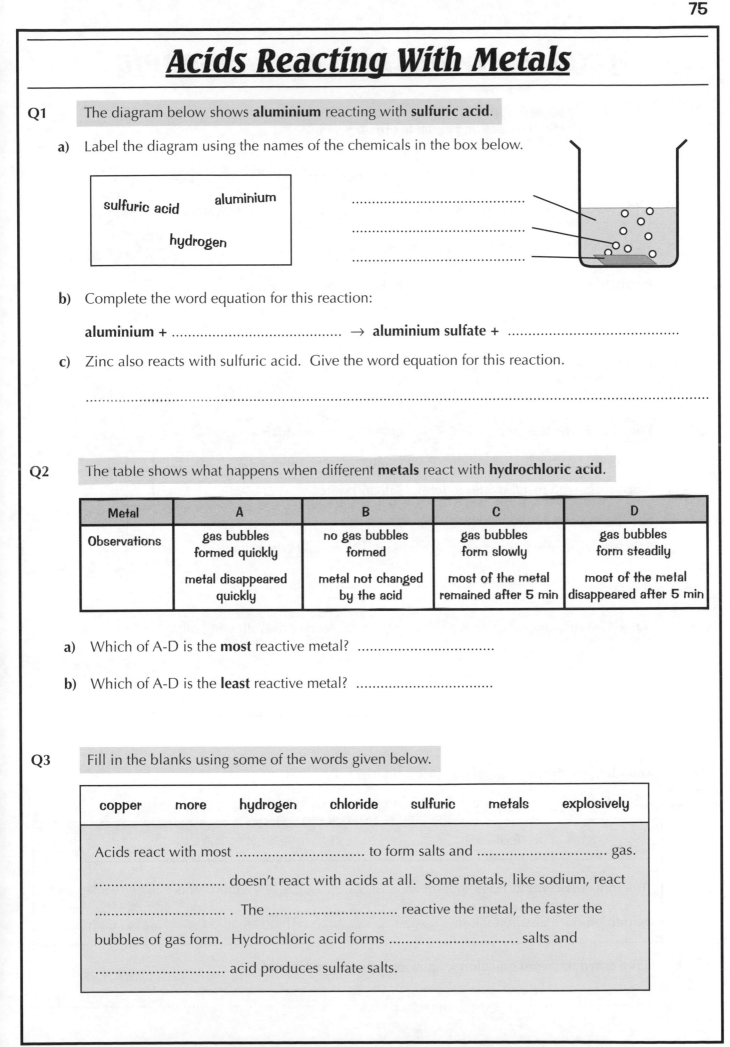

> sulfuric acid   aluminium
>
>   hydrogen

....

....

....

b)   Complete the word equation for this reaction:

aluminium + ... → **aluminium sulfate** + ...

c)   Zinc also reacts with sulfuric acid. Give the word equation for this reaction.

....

Q2   The table shows what happens when different **metals** react with **hydrochloric acid**.

Metal	A	B	C	D
Observations	gas bubbles formed quickly metal disappeared quickly	no gas bubbles formed metal not changed by the acid	gas bubbles form slowly most of the metal remained after 5 min	gas bubbles form steadily most of the metal disappeared after 5 min

a)   Which of A-D is the **most** reactive metal? ....

b)   Which of A-D is the **least** reactive metal? ....

Q3   Fill in the blanks using some of the words given below.

> copper   more   hydrogen   chloride   sulfuric   metals   explosively

Acids react with most .... to form salts and .... gas.

.... doesn't react with acids at all. Some metals, like sodium, react

.... The .... reactive the metal, the faster the

bubbles of gas form. Hydrochloric acid forms .... salts and

.... acid produces sulfate salts.

Oxides, Hydroxides and Ammonia

Q1 Fill in the blanks to complete the word equations for **acids** reacting with **metal oxides** and **metal hydroxides**.

a) hydrochloric acid + lead oxide → .... chloride + water

b) nitric acid + copper hydroxide → copper .... + water

c) sulfuric acid + zinc oxide → zinc sulfate + ...

d) hydrochloric acid + ... oxide → nickel .... + ...

e) .... acid + copper oxide → .... nitrate + ...

f) sulfuric acid + ... hydroxide → sodium .... + ...

Q2 Put a tick in the box next to any of the sentences below which are **true**.

Alkalis are bases which don't dissolve in water.

Acids react with metal oxides to form a salt and water.

Hydrogen gas is formed when an acid reacts with an alkali.

Salts and water are formed when acids react with metal hydroxides.

Q3 Name two substances which would react to make each of the following **salts**.

a) Potassium sulfate ....

b) Silver nitrate ....

Q4 **Ammonia** can be neutralised by **nitric acid** to form a salt.

a) Fill in the blanks in the passage below using the words from the list.

fertilisers	salt	alkaline
Ammonia dissolves in water to form an .... solution. This can be reacted with acid to produce an ammonium .... These are good		

b) Write down the word equation for making **ammonium nitrate**.

....

Chemistry 2b — Reaction Rates, Salts and Electrolysis

Making Salts

Q1 Complete the following sentences by circling the correct word from each pair.

a) Most chlorides, sulfates and nitrates are **soluble** / **insoluble** in water.

b) Most oxides and hydroxides are **soluble** / **insoluble** in water.

c) Soluble salts can be made by reacting **acids** / **alkalis** with insoluble bases until they are just **neutralised** / **displaced**.

d) Insoluble salts are made by **precipitation** / **electrolysis**.

Q2 The following salts can be made using **precipitation** reactions.

Choose the solutions you would need to make them from the box.
You'll need to use some of the solutions twice.

lead nitrate   magnesium sulfate   sodium chloride   sodium carbonate

a) lead sulfate: .... + ...

b) lead chloride: .... + ...

c) magnesium carbonate: .... + ...

Q3 **Silver chloride** is an insoluble salt. It is formed as a **precipitate** when silver nitrate and sodium chloride solutions are mixed together.

a) Complete the word equation for the reaction.

.... + ... → silver chloride + ...

b) After mixing the solutions to get a precipitate, what still needs to be done to get a dry sample of silver chloride?

....

....

c) Precipitation reactions can be used to remove unwanted ions from solutions. One example of this is in the treatment of sewage. Give another example.

....

Top Tips: Be prepared. The examiner might ask you to work out how to make a given salt. Don't sweat it — just pick two substances that contain the right ions. For example, to make lead chloride you're going to need lead ions and chloride ions. Don't forget that the method you use depends on whether the salt you're making is soluble or insoluble... so like I say, be prepared.

Chemistry 2b — Reaction Rates, Salts and Electrolysis

Making Salts

Q4   **Nickel sulfate** (a soluble salt) can be made by adding an excess of insoluble **nickel oxide** to **sulfuric acid** until the reaction has finished.

a)   Tick the correct box to show how you could tell that the reaction is over.

The reaction mixture changes colour.   ☐

The excess solid sinks to the bottom of the flask.   ☐

Once the reaction is over, the excess nickel oxide can be filtered from the nickel sulfate solution using the equipment shown below.

b)   Use the words below to label the diagram on the right.

....

....

....

nickel oxide
funnel
nickel sulfate solution

c)   Describe how you could get solid crystals of nickel sulfate from the nickel sulfate solution.

....

....

d)   Which other insoluble substance(s) could be reacted with sulfuric acid to make **nickel sulfate** using this method? Circle the correct answer(s) below.

nickel   lead chloride   ammonium sulfate   nickel hydroxide

e)   **Potassium sulfate** can be made by adding potassium hydroxide, an **alkali**, to sulfuric acid.

i)   Explain why the method used to make nickel sulfate couldn't be used for this reaction.

....

....

Remember an alkali is a soluble base.

ii) Describe how the method would need to be changed.

....

....

....

....

Electrolysis

Q1 Fill in the blanks in the passage below using the words provided.

You'll need to use one of the words twice.

electric current	ions	electrolysis	molten
electricity	elements	ionic	dissolved

When an ionic substance is .... or ....,

the .... are free to move about in the liquid or solution.

This lets the liquid or solution conduct ....

If you pass an .... through an ....

substance that's .... or in solution, it breaks down into the

.... it's made of. This is called ....

Q2 **Lead bromide** is an ionic substance. It doesn't dissolve easily in water.

a) How could lead bromide be made into a liquid for electrolysis?

....

b) Give the **products** of the electrolysis of lead bromide.

1. ....   2. ....

c) Tick the correct boxes to show whether the following statements about the electrolysis of **lead bromide** are **true** or **false**.

True False

i) The liquid lead bromide is the electrolyte. ☐ ☐

ii) Positively charged ions move to the positive electrode. ☐ ☐

iii) Negative bromide ions gain electrons at the positive electrode. ☐ ☐

iv) At the negative electrode, positively charged ions gain electrons. ☐ ☐

v) Oxidation is a gain of electrons. ☐ ☐

vi) Lead atoms become positive lead ions at the negative electrode. ☐ ☐

Top Tips: In chemistry, just like in love, opposites attract. Remember that when you're sat in an exam trying to work out which ions move to which electrode in an electrolysis question.

Electrolysis of Sodium Chloride Solution

Q1 Use the words below to complete the passage about the electrolysis of **sodium chloride solution**.

chlorine	sodium chloride	sodium hydroxide	plastics	bleach	
soap					negative electrode

During electrolysis, ... is split into three products.

At the positive electrode .... gas is produced. This can be used in

the production of .... and ....

At the .... hydrogen gas is given off. ....

is left in solution. This is used to make ....

Q2 The diagram below shows the electrolysis of a **salt solution**.

a) State whether ions A and B have a **positive** or a **negative** charge.

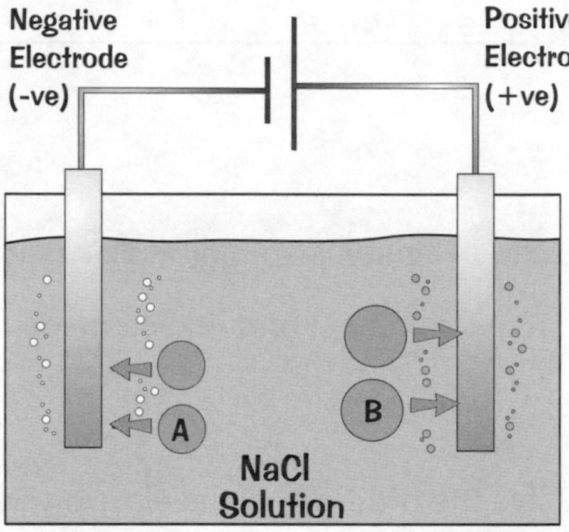

A ....

B ....

b) Draw lines to match the process to the electrode.

Oxidation	Positive electrode
Reduction	Negative electrode

Negative Electrode (-ve)   Positive Electrode (+ve)

A   B

NaCl Solution

Q3 The table shows the products at the negative electrode when different solutions of **ionic substances** are electrolysed.

a) What do you notice about the product released at the negative electrode and its position in the reactivity series?

....

....

....

....

Ionic Substance in Solution	Product at Negative Electrode
potassium chloride	hydrogen
sodium nitrate	hydrogen
zinc iodide	hydrogen
copper sulfate	copper
silver nitrate	silver

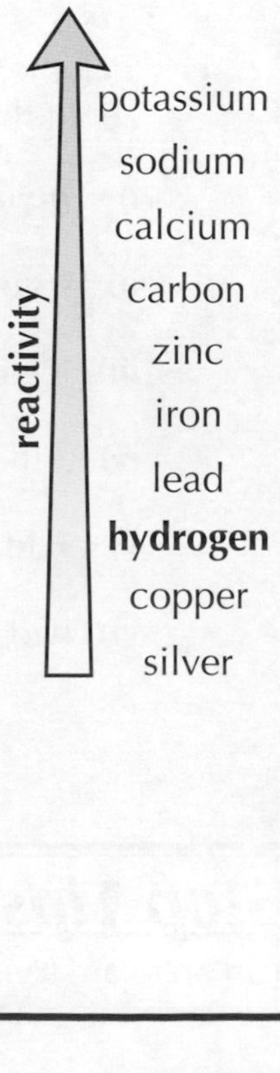

reactivity →

potassium
sodium
calcium
carbon
zinc
iron
lead
hydrogen
copper
silver

b) A solution of iron chloride is electrolysed.
What product would form at the negative electrode? Circle your answer.

hydrogen   iron

Extraction of Aluminium and Electroplating

Q1   **Aluminium** can be extracted from **aluminium oxide** using electrolysis.

a)   Tick the boxes to show whether the following statements are **true** or **false**.

                                                                                       True False

    i)   It is very easy to melt aluminium oxide.

    ii) Aluminium oxide is dissolved in molten cryolite before electrolysis begins.

    iii) Cryolite is used in the electrolysis of aluminium to make it cheaper.

    iv) Copper electrodes are used in the extraction of aluminium by electrolysis.

    v) Aluminium is formed at the negative electrode.

b) **i)**   Give the product formed at the positive electrode.

        ....

    ii) Some of this product then reacts to make **carbon dioxide**.
          Circle the correct words from the list below to show what it reacts with.

          the cryolite   the electrode   the aluminium

Q2   Electroplating could be used to put a thin coat of **silver** onto a **nickel** fork.

a)   Complete the diagram below by labelling the **negative electrode** and **positive electrode**.

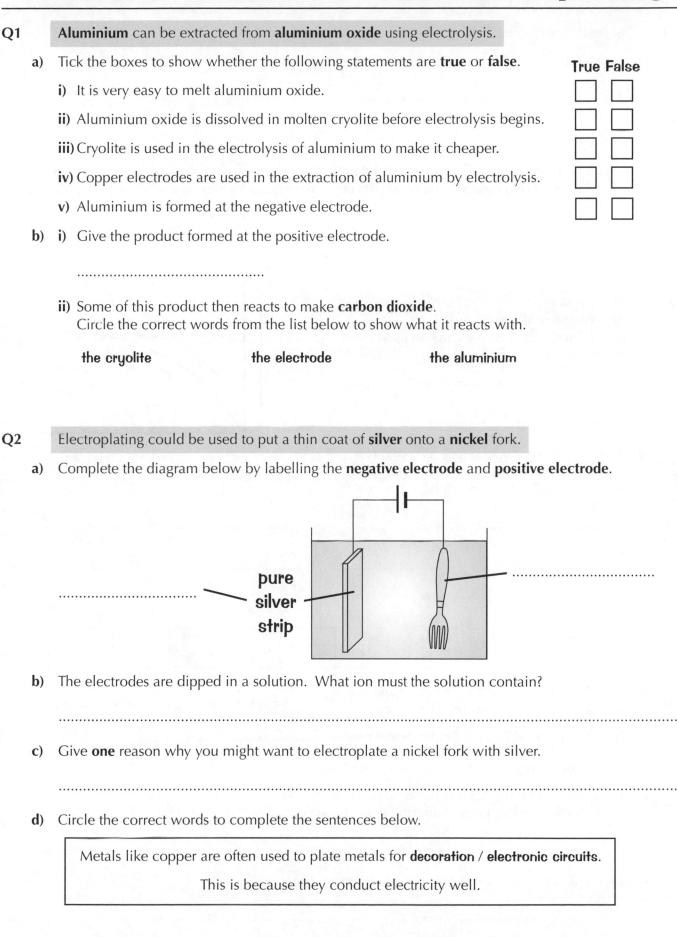

pure
silver
strip

b)   The electrodes are dipped in a solution. What ion must the solution contain?

      ....

c)   Give **one** reason why you might want to electroplate a nickel fork with silver.

      ....

d)   Circle the correct words to complete the sentences below.

> Metals like copper are often used to plate metals for **decoration / electronic circuits**.
>
> This is because they conduct electricity well.

Mixed Questions — Chemistry 2b

Q1 Several factors affect **how quickly** chemical reactions occur.

a) Name four things that can **increase** the rate of a reaction.

1. .... 2. ....

3. .... 4. ....

b) Measuring the **amount of reactant used up** over time is one way to work out the rate of a reaction. Give the other thing that can be measured over time to give the rate of a reaction.

....

Q2 The graph shows the results from an experiment using magnesium and dilute hydrochloric acid. The **change in mass** of the reactants was measured using a balance.

a) Which reaction was **faster**, P or Q?

....

b) The reaction produces a **gas**. Which other experimental method could you have used to measure the rate of reaction?

....

....

Q3 The diagram shows the **pH scale**.

| 1 | 2 | 3 | 4 | 5 | 6 | 7 | 8 | 9 | 10 | 11 | 12 | 13 |

↑ black coffee   ↑ milk of magnesia

a) The pH values of black coffee and milk of magnesia are marked on the diagram.

i) Is black coffee neutral, acidic or alkaline? ....

ii) Is milk of magnesia neutral, acidic or alkaline? ....

b) **i)** Some milk of magnesia is added to some black coffee. A reaction takes place. Name the type of reaction.

....

ii) Would this reaction be exothermic or endothermic?

....

Mixed Questions — Chemistry 2b

Q4 Circle the correct words to explain why **cryolite** is used in the electrolysis of aluminium oxide.

Aluminium oxide has a very **high** / **low** melting point. So melting it for electrolysis

would be very **expensive** / **cheap**. Instead it is **boiled** / **dissolved** in molten cryolite.

This **increases** / **decreases** the temperature needed which makes it **more expensive** / **cheaper**.

Q5 Some solid **magnesium oxide** was added to **hydrochloric acid** in a test tube. The reactants and the products are shown below. **D** is a mystery product.

magnesium oxide + hydrochloric acid → D + water

a) Name substance D. ....

b) When solid **magnesium oxide** was added to a substance, **S**, **magnesium sulfate** and **water** were formed. Name substance S.

....

c) State whether metal oxides are **acids** or **bases**. ....

Q6 The electrolysis of **sodium chloride solution** gives useful products that can be used in industry.

a) Circle the substance that forms at the positive **electrode**.

sodium   chlorine   oxygen

b) i) At the negative electrode, hydrogen is formed. Explain why hydrogen is formed and not sodium.   ⌐Talk about reactivity⌐ in your answer.

....

....

....

ii) Is hydrogen oxidised or reduced at the negative electrode?

....

c) Electrolysis is also used for electroplating. What is electroplating?

....

Velocity and Distance-Time Graphs

Q1 Draw lines to match speed and velocity to their correct description.

Speed

How fast you're going in a given direction.

Velocity

How fast you're going — the direction doesn't matter.

Q2 A theme park **monorail** takes people between the visitor centre and the main park. It travels at the same **speed** on the outward and return journeys.

The monorail's velocity on the outward journey is 12 m/s west. What is its velocity on the return journey?

....

Buffers' Theme Park

| Monorail | Visitor centre |
| Main park | River | Car park |

Q3 Steve walked to football training only to find that he'd left his boots at home. He turned round and walked back home, where he spent 30 seconds looking for them. To make it to training on time he had to run back at twice his walking speed.

Below is an incomplete **distance-time graph** for Steve's journey.

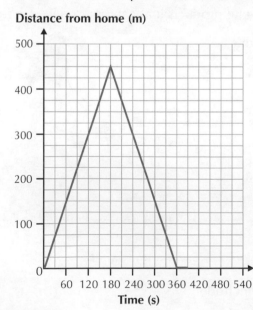

Distance from home (m)

Time (s)

a) How long did it take Steve to walk to training?

....

b) How far away from the training ground does Steve live?

....

c) Complete the graph to show Steve's run back from his house to training (with his boots).

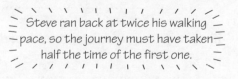

Steve ran back at twice his walking pace, so the journey must have taken half the time of the first one.

Top Tips: Velocity and speed are pretty much used to mean the same thing in everyday language, but in physics you need to make sure you know the difference between them — so get learning.

Acceleration and Velocity-Time Graphs

Q1   A model car accelerates from rest to 20 m/s in **3.5 s**.

a)   What is the formula for acceleration? Circle the correct answer.

$$a = \frac{v - t}{u} \qquad a = \frac{v - u}{t} \qquad a = \frac{t - u}{u} \qquad a = \frac{t - u}{v}$$

b)   Calculate the acceleration of the model car.
Give units with your answer.

If the car accelerates from rest, its initial velocity is 0.

....

....

Q2   Match the **type of motion** in the box on the right to each of the **labelled sections** of the **velocity-time graph**. One has been done for you.

| acceleration |
| deceleration |
| constant speed |

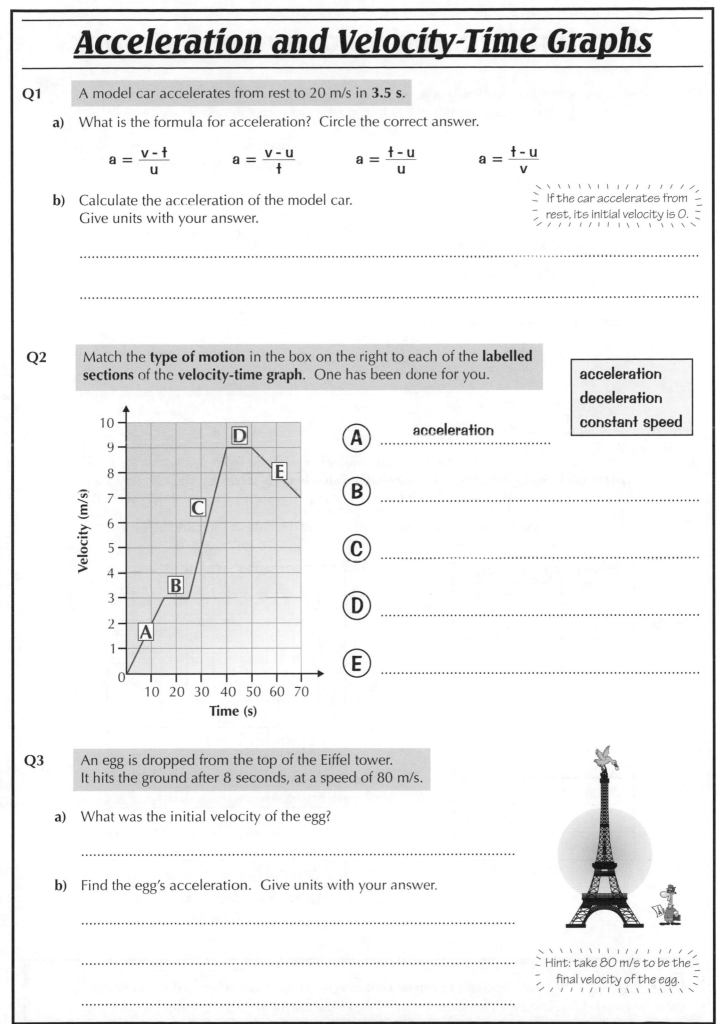

(A) ......acceleration......................

(B) ....

(C) ....

(D) ....

(E) ....

Q3   An egg is dropped from the top of the Eiffel tower.
It hits the ground after 8 seconds, at a speed of 80 m/s.

a)   What was the initial velocity of the egg?

....

b)   Find the egg's acceleration. Give units with your answer.

....

....

Hint: take 80 m/s to be the final velocity of the egg.

Acceleration and Velocity-Time Graphs

Q4 Below is a set of velocity-time graphs for a spaceship landing on three different planets, **A**, **B** and **C**. It accelerates due to the pull of gravity from the planets.

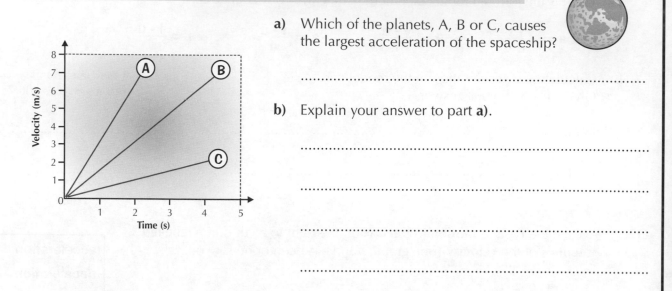

a) Which of the planets, A, B or C, causes the largest acceleration of the spaceship?

....

b) Explain your answer to part **a)**.

....

....

....

....

Q5 A cyclist records his velocity of **every 5 seconds**. He speeds up **from rest** with a **constant acceleration**. He cycles at **maximum velocity for 5 seconds**. Then he slows down to a stop with a **constant deceleration**. The bike stays **at rest** for the **last 5 seconds**.

Plot a velocity-time graph of the cyclist's journey using the data in the table below.

Time (s)	Velocity (m/s)
0	0
5	4
10	8
15	12
20	12
25	9
30	6
35	3
40	0
45	0

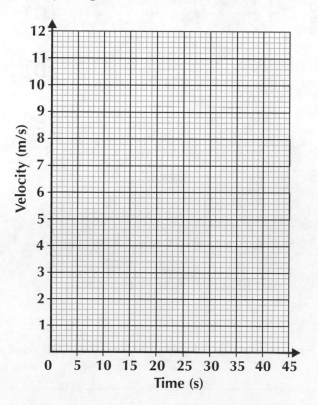

Top Tips: Velocity-time graphs can be confusing — so don't rush them. Take your time to break the graph down into the different sections and figure out exactly what's happening at each stage.

Weight, Mass and Gravity

Q1 Fill in the gaps in the following paragraph using the words below.

kilograms	newtons	mass	weight	gravitational

The .... of an object is just the amount of 'stuff' it's made up of. It doesn't

change, regardless of where in the Universe it is, and it's measured in ....

.... is a force and is measured in ....

It's the .... force that one object exerts on another.

Q2 An astronaut goes to Mars to do some experiments.

a) Complete the paragraph below by circling the correct words in each pair.

When the astronaut goes to Mars her **mass / weight** stays the same

but her **mass / weight** changes. This is because the strength of

gravity / electrostatic repulsion on Mars is **the same as / different to** that on Earth.

b) The **gravitational field strength** on Mars is **3.8 N/kg**. On Earth it is **10 N/kg**. $W = m \times g$

i) Calculate the weight of a 5 kg mass on Mars.

....

ii) Calculate the weight of a 5 kg mass on Earth.

....

Q3 Joni has been feeding her dog Fluffy a bit too much. The vet decides he needs to go on a diet.   Use g = 10 N/kg

a) Joni puts Fluffy on some scales and finds he has a mass of **58 kg**. Calculate his **weight**.

....

b) After three weeks of eating only 'Skinny Dog' biscuits, Fluffy's mass has gone down to **49 kg**. Calculate his new weight.

....

....

Top Tips: Gravity may be keeping you down on the Earth, but it's **surprisingly weak**. Think about it — you have the whole Earth pulling you downwards but you can jump and hop and skip away from it without too much effort. The fact is, **anything that has mass has gravity**, but objects have to be pretty huge before anyone notices.

Resultant Forces

Q1   A teapot sits on a table.

a)   Complete the sentences below by circling the correct word in each pair.

> The teapot's **weight** / **mass** is balanced by the **gravitational** / **reaction** force from the table. Since the forces are **equal** / **different** sizes in the **opposite** / **same** direction, the teapot remains stationary.

b)   The teapot has a weight of 15 N acting downwards.

   i)   What is the size of the force acting upwards on the teapot from the table?

   ....

   ii)   What is the size of the resultant force on the teapot?

   ....

Q2   A bear rides a bike.

a)   Label the forces acting on the bear. Use words from the box.

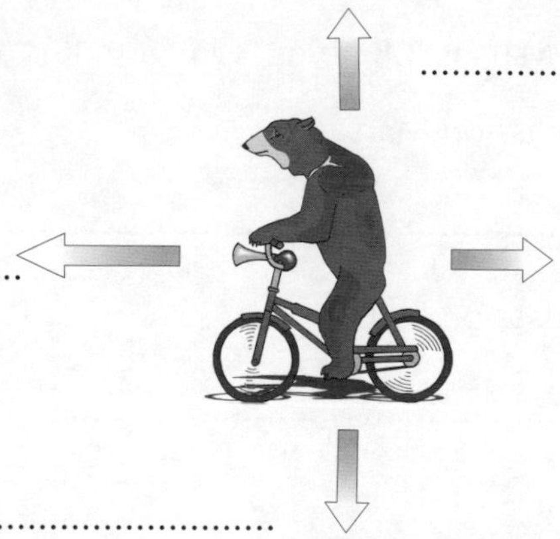

| Reaction |
| Driving Force |
| Weight |
| Air Resistance |

....

....

....

b)   The force moving the bike forwards is **500 N**. The backwards force on the bike is **200 N**.
Draw and label an arrow on the diagram above to show the size and direction of the resultant force.

Q3   The **force diagram** on the right shows a **train** pulling out of a station.

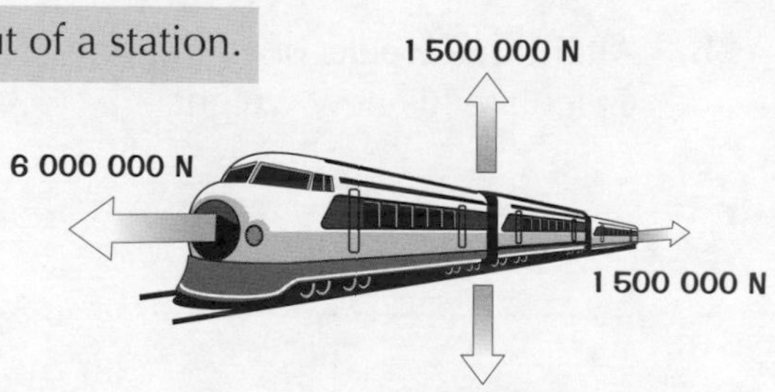

1 500 000 N

6 000 000 N

a)   Calculate the resultant force acting on the train in the following directions:

1 500 000 N

   i) Vertical: ....

   ii) Horizontal: ....

1 500 000 N

b)   Is the train moving at a steady velocity? Explain your answer.

....

....

Forces and Acceleration

Q1 Use the words in the box to fill in the blanks in the paragraph below.

resultant	stationary	accelerates	constant

If the forces on an object are balanced , it's either ………….…..……….. or moving

at ………….…..……….. speed. If an object has a non-zero resultant force acting

on it, it ………….…..…......... in the direction of the ………..…..……….. force.

Q2 You're travelling home from school on a bus doing a steady speed in a straight line.
Which of the following statements are **true**? Tick the correct box(es).

☐ The forwards driving force of the engine is bigger than the forces acting backwards.

☐ The forwards driving force of the engine is equal to the forces acting backwards.

☐ A resultant force is required to keep the bus moving.

☐ There must be no resultant force acting on the bus.

Q3 The diagram below shows the **forces** acting on a plane.

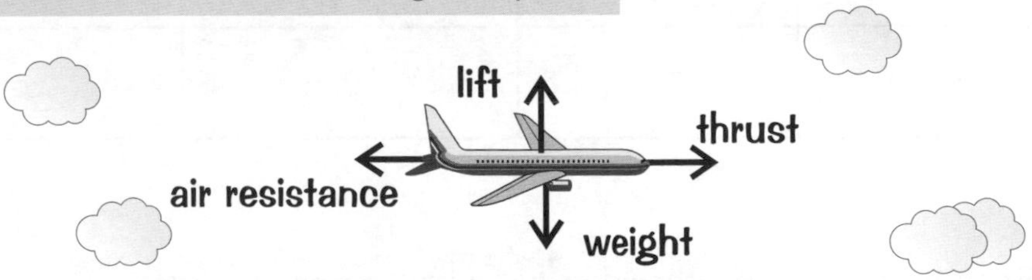

a) The plane is flying horizontally at a constant speed of 200 m/s.
Which of the following statements about the plane is true? Circle the correct letter.

  A The thrust is bigger than the air resistance and the lift is bigger than the weight.

  B The thrust is smaller than the air resistance and the lift is equal to the weight.

  C The thrust is equal to the air resistance and the lift is equal to the weight.

b) What happens to the forces as the plane **descends** for landing and **slows down** to 100 m/s?
Circle the correct words to complete the following statements:

  i) The thrust is **greater than / less than / equal to** the air resistance.

  ii) The lift is **greater than / less than / equal to** the weight.

Remember — the plane is losing height as well as slowing down.

Forces and Acceleration

Q4   Which of the following statements explains what happens when you walk? Tick the correct box.

☐   Your feet push backwards on the ground, so the ground pushes you forwards.

☐   The force in your muscles is greater than the
          backwards forces between your feet and the ground.

☐   Your feet work against the reaction force from
          the ground, which is pushing you backwards.

☐   Your feet push forwards, and the ground's reaction is upwards.

Q5   The maximum acceleration of four cars is shown in the table below.
         Complete the table to show the resultant force on the cars at their maximum acceleration.

$F = m \times a$

Car	Mass (kg)	Maximum acceleration (m/s²)	Force (N)
Disraeli 9000	800	5	
Palmerston 6i	1560	0.7	
Heath TT	950	3	
Asquith 380	790	2	

Q6   Jo and Brian have fitted both their scooters with the **same engine**.
         Brian and his scooter have a combined mass of **110 kg** and a maximum
         acceleration of **2.80 m/s²**. The combined mass of Jo and her scooter is **160 kg**.

a)   Calculate the maximum **force** the engine can exert.

....

....

b)   Calculate the **maximum acceleration** of Jo and her scooter. $a = F \div m$

....

....

Physics 2a — Motion, Energy and Electricity

Frictional Force and Drag

Q1 Use the words supplied to fill in the blanks in the paragraph below about friction.

stop	steady speed	fluid	equal	driving force	space

When an object passes through a .... , friction acts in the opposite

direction to the direction of movement. If an object has no ....

acting on it, friction will cause it to slow down and eventually ....

This isn't true in .... because there is no air or other fluid providing

something to rub against, so there is no friction. When an object is moving at a

.... the driving force is .... to the friction.

Q2 Which of the following will **reduce** the air resistance force on an aeroplane? Tick all the correct boxes.

☐ **flying higher (where the air is thinner)**   ☐ **carrying less cargo**

☐ **flying more slowly**   ☐ **making the plane more streamlined**

Q3 A camper van is driven along a straight, level road at different speeds on four different days. There is no wind, and the road conditions are exactly the same every day.

a) The diagrams below show the camper van on each of the four days. On which day would the camper van experience the **largest frictional force**? Circle the correct diagram.

20 mph →   ← 40 mph   50 mph →   30 mph →

Day 1   **Day 2**   **Day 3**   **Day 4**

b) Explain your answer to part **a)**.

....

....

....

Terminal Velocity

Q1 A scientist plans to investigate gravity by dropping a hammer and a feather from a tall building. Two onlookers predict what will happen. Say whether each is right or wrong, and explain why.

Paola: "They will land at the same time — gravity is the same for both."

Guiseppe: "The feather will reach its terminal velocity before the hammer."

a) Paola is **right** / **wrong** because ....

....

....

b) Guiseppe is **right** / **wrong** because ....

....

....

Q2 The graph shows how the velocity of a skydiver changes before and after he opens his parachute.

a) For each of the four regions A-D tick the correct box to say whether the force of **weight** or **air resistance** is greater, or if they are **equal**.

	weight is greater	air resistance is greater	both equal
Region A:	☐	☐	☐
Region B:	☐	☐	☐
Region C:	☐	☐	☐
Region D:	☐	☐	☐

b) Explain why the parachute lets the skydiver fall at a **lower velocity**.

....

....

Top Tips: When objects move through the air at high speed, the air resistance is proportional to the object's **velocity squared**. That's why, for skydivers, air resistance soon balances their weight and they reach terminal velocity. It's also why **driving** very fast is very **inefficient**.

Stopping Distances

Q1 **Stopping distance**, **braking distance** and **thinking distance** aren't the same things. Complete the definitions below by circling the correct words.

a) Braking distance is the distance the car travels under the **braking force / driving force** before it comes to a stop.

b) Thinking distance is the distance the car travels during the driver's **braking time / reaction time**.

c) Stopping distance is the **difference between / sum of** the thinking distance and braking distance.

Q2 Will the following factors affect **thinking** distance, **braking** distance or **both**? Write them in the correct columns of the table.

tiredness

road surface

weather

drugs

distractions

brakes

alcohol

tyres

speed

Thinking Distance	Braking Distance

Some factors can be used in both columns.

Q3 A car joins a motorway and changes speed from 30 mph to 60 mph. Which of the following statements are **true**? Tick the correct boxes.

☐ The total stopping distance will increase.

☐ The braking force needed to stop in a certain distance will decrease.

☐ Thinking distance will decrease.

☐ Both thinking and braking distance will increase.

94

Work Done

Q1 Circle the correct words to make the following sentences true.

a) Work involves the transfer of **force** / **energy**.

b) To do work, **a force** / **an acceleration** must act over a **distance** / **time**.

c) Work is measured in **watts** / **joules**.

Q2 Tick the boxes to show whether the following statements are **true** or **false**.

	True	False
a) Work is done when a toy car is pushed along the ground.	☺	☹
b) No work is done if a force is applied to an object which does not move.	☺	☹
c) The force of gravity does work on an apple that is not moving.	☺	☹
d) The force of gravity does work on an apple that falls out of a tree.	☺	☹

Q3 An elephant exerts a constant force of **1200 N** to push a donkey along a track. $W = F \times d$

a) Calculate the work done by the elephant if the donkey moves **8 m**.

....

....

b) From where does the elephant get the energy to do this work?

....

Q4 Joe and Fred put two identical barrels into a lorry. Joe rolls one barrel up a **4 m** plank by pushing with a constant force of **350 N**. Fred lifts the other barrel, which weighs **800 N**, a distance of **1.5 m** onto the lorry.

a) Calculate the work done by **Joe** on the barrel.

....

....

b) When Fred lifts his barrel, he does work against the **weight** of the barrel. Calculate the work done by **Fred** on the barrel.

....

....

Physics 2a — Motion, Energy and Electricity

Kinetic and Potential Energy

Q1   Fill in the gaps to complete the following sentences about moving objects.

All moving objects have .... energy.

This energy depends on the .... and .... of the object.

Q2   Number the following vehicles 1-3, where 1 is the vehicle having the **most kinetic energy**, and 3 is the vehicle having the **least kinetic energy**.

$E_k = \frac{1}{2} \times m \times v^2$

60 000 kg, 17 m/s   100 kg, 8 m/s   1200 kg, 15 m/s

....

Working-out space →

....

....

....

Q3   A large truck and a car both have a speed of **25 m/s**. The mass of the truck is **12 288 kg** and the car **1200 kg**.

a)   Calculate the **kinetic energy** of:

i) the car ....

ii) the truck ....

b)   The truck is driven up a hill until it is **50 m** higher up. Calculate its gain in gravitational potential energy. Use g = 10 N/kg.

$E_p = m \times g \times h$

....

....

c)   The car is driven up a hill until it is **20 m** higher up. Calculate its gain in gravitational potential energy.

....

....

Work and Kinetic Energy

Q1   Use the words supplied to fill in the blanks in the paragraph below. You will need to use some words more than once.

kinetic	heat	frictional

A space shuttle re-entering the atmosphere has a very high .... energy.

Work is done by the .... force between the shuttle and the atmosphere.

This transfers the .... energy to .... energy, making

the shuttle very hot. To stop it from burning up, the space shuttle has heat shields that are

made from special materials that lose .... quickly.

Q2   A toy cricket ball hit straight upwards has a **gravitational potential energy** of **242 J** at the **top** of its flight. What is the ball's **kinetic energy** just before it hits the ground? Explain your answer.

....

....

Q3   Jack rides his bicycle along a level road. He brakes, exerting a force of **200 N** on the wheels, and travels **7.2 m** before he stops.

$W = F \times d$

a)   Calculate the work done by the brakes to stop the bicycle.

....

....

b)   How much kinetic energy is transferred by the bike during braking?

....

c)   What happens to the temperature of the brakes? Explain your answer.

....

....

Top Tips: The main thing to remember is that **energy transferred** and **work done** are just the **same** thing. You're bound to get asked to do a calculation, so make sure you know how to use those equations. All work questions are pretty similar — so just keep practising and you'll be fine.

Physics 2a — Motion, Energy and Electricity

Forces and Elasticity

Q1 Alice is bouncing on a trampoline.

a) Complete the paragraph below by circling the correct word in each pair.

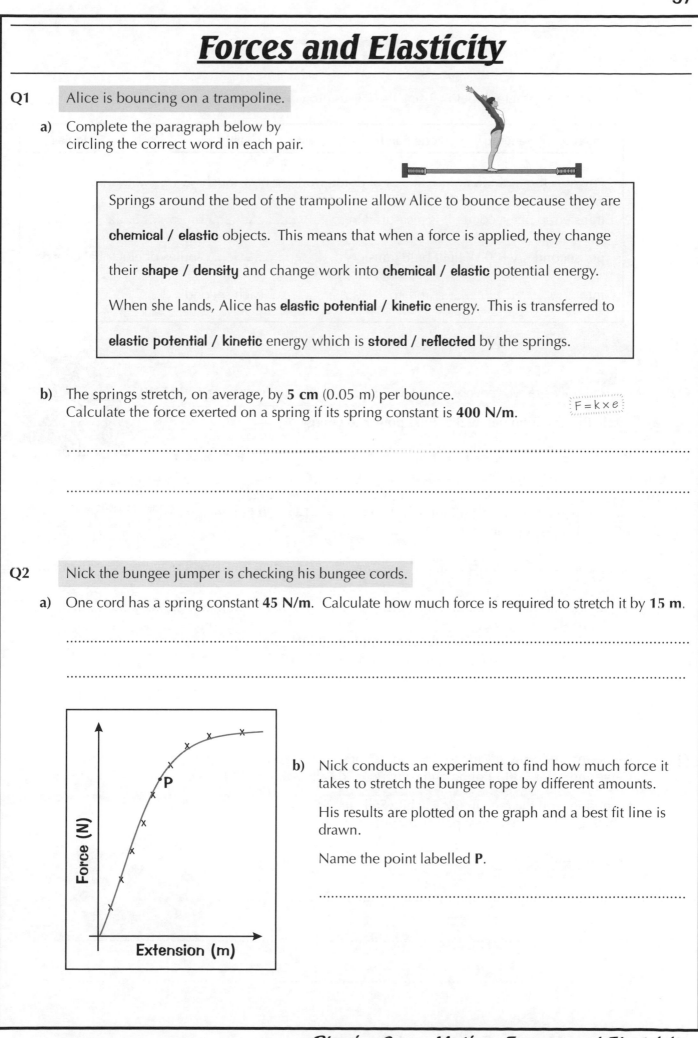

> Springs around the bed of the trampoline allow Alice to bounce because they are
>
> **chemical / elastic** objects. This means that when a force is applied, they change
>
> their **shape / density** and change work into **chemical / elastic** potential energy.
>
> When she lands, Alice has **elastic potential / kinetic** energy. This is transferred to
>
> **elastic potential / kinetic** energy which is **stored / reflected** by the springs.

b) The springs stretch, on average, by **5 cm** (0.05 m) per bounce.
Calculate the force exerted on a spring if its spring constant is **400 N/m**.

$F = k \times e$

....

....

Q2 Nick the bungee jumper is checking his bungee cords.

a) One cord has a spring constant **45 N/m**. Calculate how much force is required to stretch it by **15 m**.

....

....

b) Nick conducts an experiment to find how much force it takes to stretch the bungee rope by different amounts.

His results are plotted on the graph and a best fit line is drawn.

Name the point labelled **P**.

....

98

Power

Q1 Complete the paragraph below using the words provided.

heat	energy	one hundred	rate	light	watts	joules

Power is the .... of doing work, or how much .... is

transferred per second. It is measured in .... or ....

per second. A 100 W light bulb transfers .... joules of electrical energy

into .... and .... each second.

Q2 George drives to work every day in a small car with a **power** output of **50 kW**.

a) Circle the equation below that links **power** to **energy**.

$P = t \div E$ $E = P \div t$ $P = E \div t$ $P = E \times t$

b) One day George's car breaks down and so he cycles to work.
The journey takes him **12 minutes** and he transfers **144 000 J** of energy.
What is his power output?

Remember to convert minutes into seconds first. 1 minute = 60 seconds.

....

....

c) George buys a new car with a power output of **75 kW**.
How will its top speed compare with that of his old car?

....

Q3 Catherine and Sally decide to run up a set of stairs to see who can get to the top fastest.
Catherine gains **2300 J** of potential energy and Sally gains **2400 J**.

Catherine won the race in **6.2 s**, while Sally took **6.4 s**.
Which girl had the biggest **power output**?

....

....

....

....

Momentum and Collisions

Q1   Circle the correct words to make the following statements true.

a)   If the velocity of a moving object doubles, its **kinetic energy** / **momentum** will double.

b)   If you drop a suitcase out of a moving car, the car's momentum will **decrease** / **increase**.

c)   When two objects collide the total momentum **changes** / **stays the same**.

d)   When a force acts on an object its momentum **changes** / **stays the same**.

Q2   Place the following four trucks in order of increasing momentum.

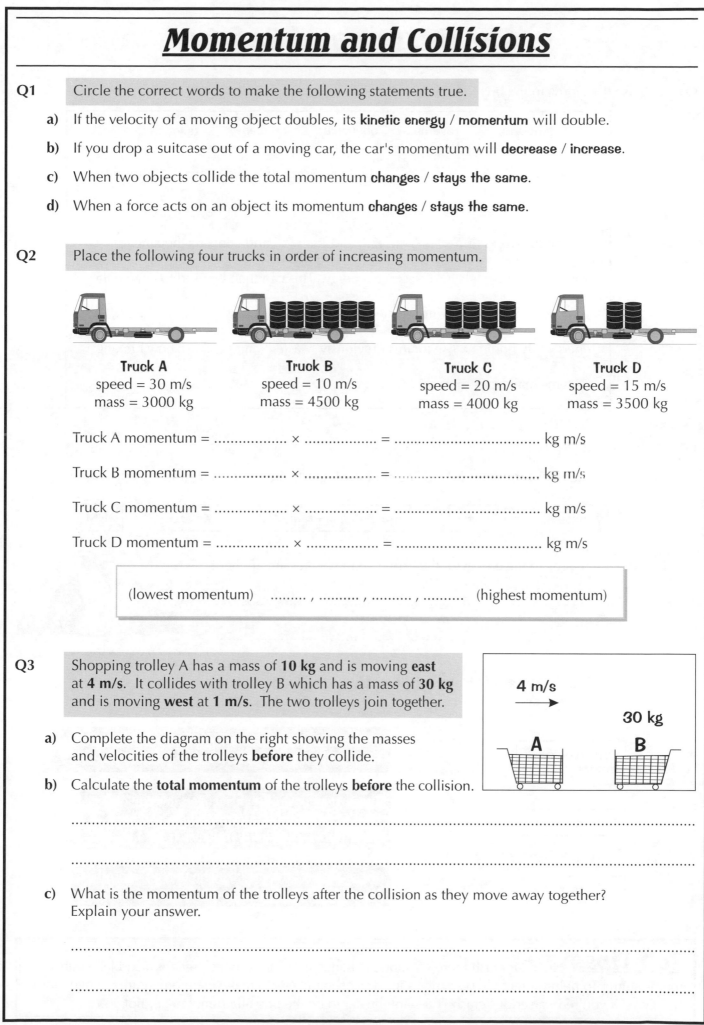

Truck A	Truck B	Truck C	Truck D
speed = 30 m/s	speed = 10 m/s	speed = 20 m/s	speed = 15 m/s
mass = 3000 kg	mass = 4500 kg	mass = 4000 kg	mass = 3500 kg

Truck A momentum = ... × .... = ... kg m/s

Truck B momentum = ... × .... = ... kg m/s

Truck C momentum = ... × .... = ... kg m/s

Truck D momentum = ... × .... = ... kg m/s

(lowest momentum)   .... , ... , ... , ...   (highest momentum)

Q3   Shopping trolley A has a mass of **10 kg** and is moving **east** at **4 m/s**. It collides with trolley B which has a mass of **30 kg** and is moving **west** at **1 m/s**. The two trolleys join together.

a)   Complete the diagram on the right showing the masses and velocities of the trolleys **before** they collide.

b)   Calculate the **total momentum** of the trolleys **before** the collision.

....

....

c)   What is the momentum of the trolleys after the collision as they move away together? Explain your answer.

....

....

Car Design and Safety

Q1   Use the words in the box to fill in the gaps in the paragraph below.

generator	reverse	chemical	efficient	regenerative

New .... braking systems put the vehicle's motor into

.... to slow the wheels down during braking.

The motor works as a .... and converts the kinetic

energy of the wheels into electrical energy. This can then be used to charge the

vehicle's battery — storing the electrical energy as ....

energy. By finding a use for this previously 'wasted' energy, these new braking

systems make cars more ....

Q2   A car travels along a level road and brakes to avoid hitting a cat.

a)   What type of **energy** does the moving car have? Circle the correct answer.

Nuclear	Elastic	Gravitational Potential	Kinetic	Light

b)   What happens to the energy of the car when the brakes are applied?

....

....

Q3   For each of the **car safety features** below, draw a line to match it to the description of the way it helps to protect passengers in a crash.

Crumple zones

Side impact bars

Airbags

These direct the kinetic energy of a crash away from the passengers and towards other parts of the car.

These slow down the passengers over a longer time to reduce the forces on them and stop them from hitting hard surfaces in the car.

These convert the car's kinetic energy into other types of energy as they squash up on impact.

Top Tips: In a car crash there's a sudden change in velocity, which means a sudden change in momentum. To help protect the passengers inside, the car needs to make the momentum change more slowly — if you're in a serious crash you want the car to be the one all crumpled up, not you.

Physics 2a — Motion, Energy and Electricity

Static Electricity

Q1 **Circle** the pairs of charges that would attract each other and **underline** those that would repel.

positive and positive   positive and negative   negative and positive   negative and negative

Q2 Fill in the gaps in these sentences with the words below.

electrons	positive	insulating	negative

Static electricity can build up when two .... materials are

rubbed together. The friction moves .... from one material

onto the other. This leaves a .... charge on one of the

materials and a .... charge on the other.

Q3 Circle the correct words to complete each sentence.

a) A polythene rod becomes negatively charged when rubbed with a duster because it **loses / gains** electrons.

b) When two charged objects are close together, they each feel a **force / current** from the other.

c) Electrical charges can't move very easily through **insulators / metals**.

d) When electrons are transferred between two materials, the positive charge on one material is **bigger than / equal to / smaller than** the negative charge on the other material.

Q4 When Russell takes off his jumper, his hair becomes electrically charged and stands on end.

a) Suggest why his hair becomes electrically charged.

....

....

b) After taking off his jumper, the hairs on his head all have the **same charge**. Explain why this causes them to stand on end.

Think about what happens when things with the same charge come together.

....

....

Physics 2a — Motion, Energy and Electricity

Current and Potential Difference

Q1   Use the words below to complete the passage.

reduces	voltage	decrease	charge	work

Electric current is the flow of electric .... around a circuit. Current flows

through a component which has a potential difference (................................) across it.

The potential difference between two points in an circuit is the .... done per

coulomb of charge that passes between the points. Resistance .... the flow

of current — to increase the current in a circuit you can .... the resistance.

Q2   Draw lines to connect the quantities with their units and the symbols of their units. The first one has been done for you.

A	Current	coulombs
V	Resistance	joules
Ω	Charge	ohms
J	Work	amps
C	Potential Difference	volts

Q3   A battery provides **6000 C** of charge in **20 minutes** before it needs recharging.

$I = Q \div t$

a)   Calculate how much current flows through the battery.

....

Convert to seconds first:
1 minute = 60 seconds

....

b)   Calculate the potential difference across the battery if it does **18 000 J** of work before it needs recharging.

$V = W \div Q$

....

....

Q4   Sally is comparing two lamps, A and B. She takes the measurements shown in the table.

Calculate the **missing values** and write them in the table.

time = 10 s

	Lamp A	Lamp B
Charge passing in 10 s (C)	20	40
Work done in 10 s (J)	60	80
Current through lamp (A)		
Potential difference across lamp (V)		

Circuits — The Basics

Q1 Complete the following passage by using the words from the box.

circuit	across	through

You can measure the resistance of a component using a standard test ....

To work out the resistance of the component, you need to measure the current

.... the component and the potential difference .... it.

Q2 Match up these items from a standard test circuit with the **correct description** and **symbol**.

ITEM	DESCRIPTION	SYMBOL
Cell	Provides the 'push' on the charge.	—(A)—
Variable Resistor	The item you're testing.	
Component	Used to alter the current.	—|⊢
Voltmeter	Measures the current.	—(V)—
Ammeter	Measures the potential difference.	

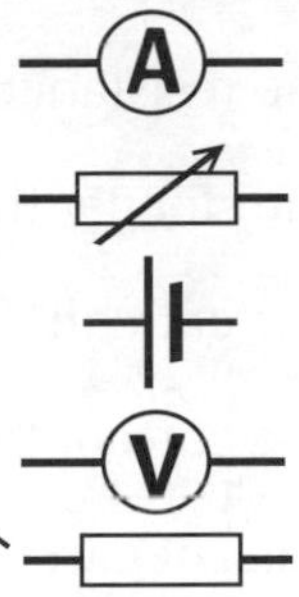

Q3 The diagram below shows a **complete circuit**.

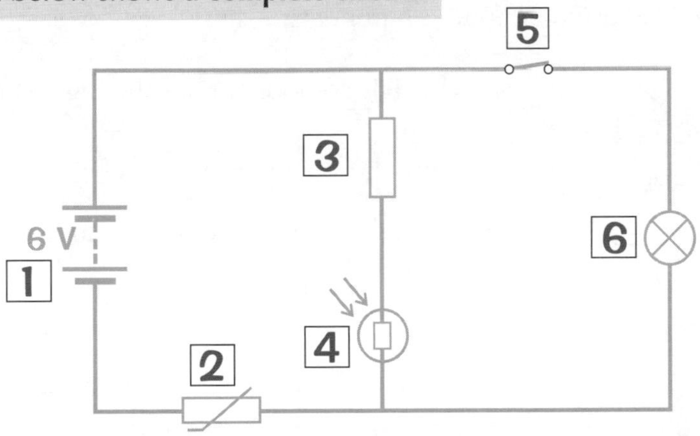

Wilkins, drop and give me ten circuits, complete with ammeter and voltmeter.

Mr Smith was keen on circuit training.

a) Give the name of each of the numbered components.

1. .... 2. ....

3. .... 4. ....

5. .... 6. ....

b) Add a symbol to the diagram in the correct position to show the item used to measure the **current** leaving the battery.

c) Add a symbol to the diagram in the correct position to show the item used to measure the **potential difference** across the lamp.

Resistance and V = I × R

Q1 Write the correct label under each of the **V-I graphs** below. Use words from the list.

RESISTOR   FILAMENT BULB   DIODE

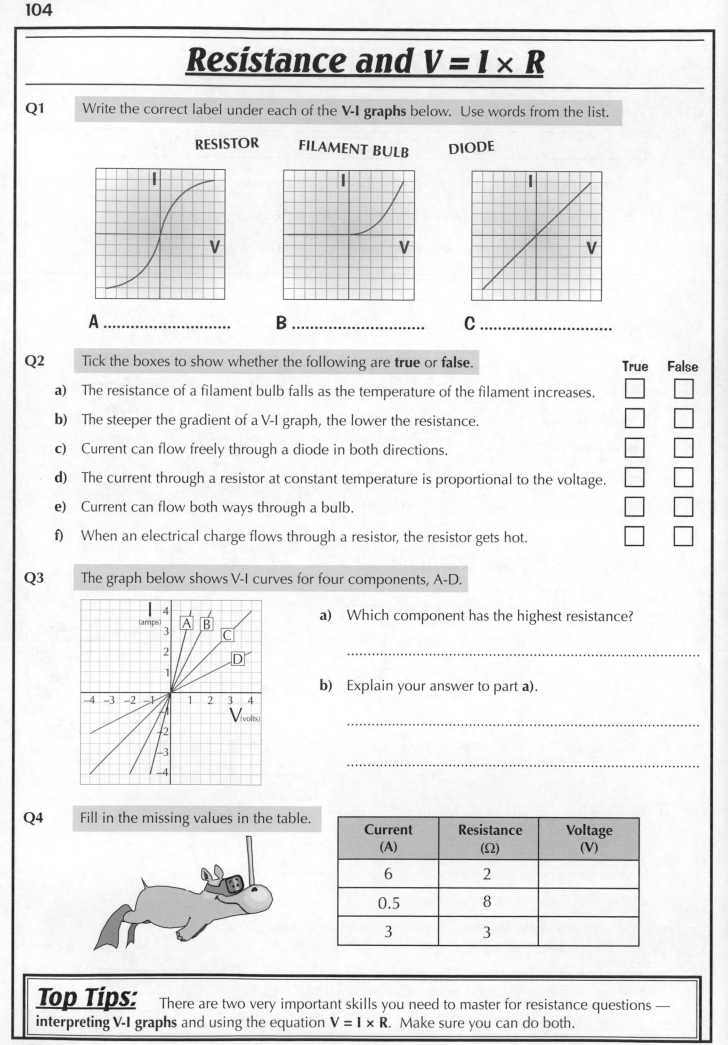

A ....   B ....   C ....

Q2 Tick the boxes to show whether the following are **true** or **false**.

		True	False
a)	The resistance of a filament bulb falls as the temperature of the filament increases.	☐	☐
b)	The steeper the gradient of a V-I graph, the lower the resistance.	☐	☐
c)	Current can flow freely through a diode in both directions.	☐	☐
d)	The current through a resistor at constant temperature is proportional to the voltage.	☐	☐
e)	Current can flow both ways through a bulb.	☐	☐
f)	When an electrical charge flows through a resistor, the resistor gets hot.	☐	☐

Q3 The graph below shows V-I curves for four components, A-D.

a) Which component has the highest resistance?

....

b) Explain your answer to part **a)**.

....

....

Q4 Fill in the missing values in the table.

Current (A)	Resistance (Ω)	Voltage (V)
6	2	
0.5	8	
3	3	

Top Tips: There are two very important skills you need to master for resistance questions — interpreting **V-I graphs** and using the equation **V = I × R**. Make sure you can do both.

Circuit Devices

Q1   Use the words below to fill in the gaps.

light-dependent	lights	thermistor	vary	thermostats

The resistance of some components can .... The resistance of a

.... goes up as the temperature decreases — this makes them useful as

electronic .... The resistance of a .... resistor

depends on the intensity of light falling on it — its resistance drops when light shines on it.

They're often used to automatically switch on .... when it gets dark.

Q2   LEDs are increasingly used for lighting.

a)   Write out what the letters **L E D** stand for.

L................................... E................................... D...................................

b)   Tick the boxes to show whether the following sentences are **true** or **false**.   **True**   **False**

   i) LEDs only emit light when a current flows in the forward direction.   ☐   ☐

   ii) LEDs are increasingly used because they use a much bigger current than other forms of lighting.   ☐   ☐

   iii) LEDs can be used to show whether a current is flowing in a circuit.   ☐   ☐

c)   Name **two** appliances that use LEDs.

   1. ....

   2. ....

LED = Last Ever Diplodocus?

Q3   A thermistor is a temperature dependent resistor.

a)   Draw the circuit symbol for a thermistor in the box below.

b)   Sketch a graph of resistance against temperature for a thermistor on the axes below.

Resistance in Ω

Temperature

Physics 2a — Motion, Energy and Electricity

Series Circuits

Q1   Match up these definitions with what they describe in a series circuit.

Same everywhere in the circuit

Shared by all the components

The sum of the resistances

Can be different for each component

Potential difference

Current

Total potential difference

Total resistance

Q2   Eva sets up the series circuit shown in the diagram:

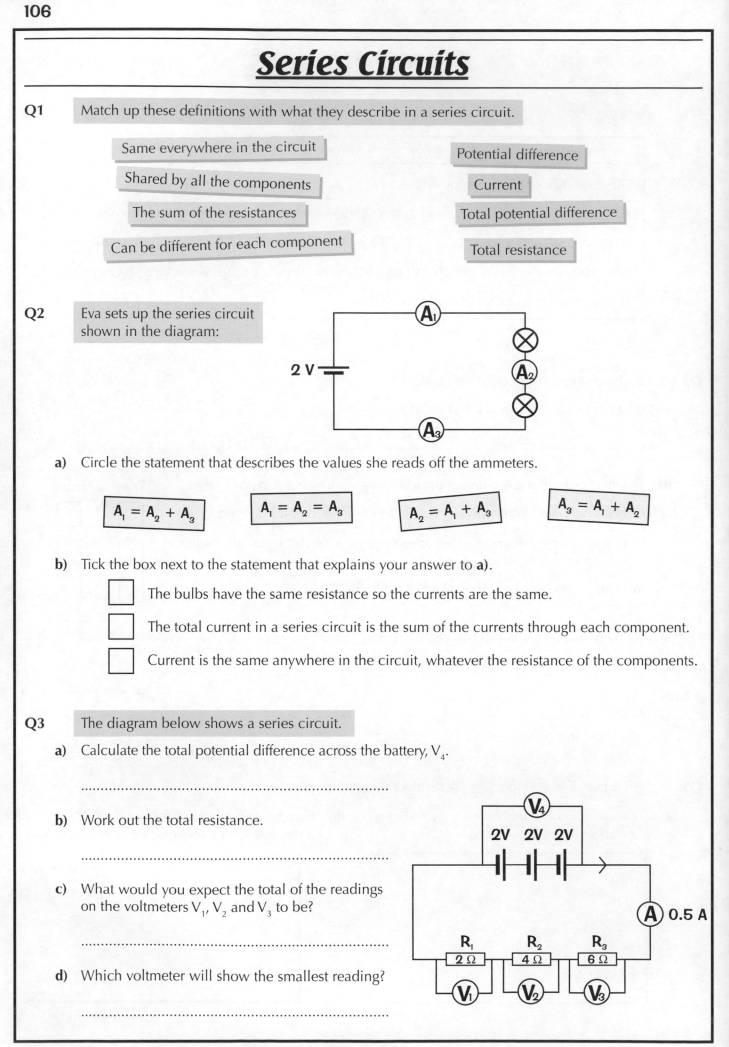

a)   Circle the statement that describes the values she reads off the ammeters.

$A_1 = A_2 + A_3$ $A_1 = A_2 = A_3$ $A_2 = A_1 + A_3$ $A_3 = A_1 + A_2$

b)   Tick the box next to the statement that explains your answer to **a)**.

☐ The bulbs have the same resistance so the currents are the same.

☐ The total current in a series circuit is the sum of the currents through each component.

☐ Current is the same anywhere in the circuit, whatever the resistance of the components.

Q3   The diagram below shows a series circuit.

a)   Calculate the total potential difference across the battery, V_4.

....

b)   Work out the total resistance.

....

c)   What would you expect the total of the readings on the voltmeters V_1, V_2 and V_3 to be?

....

d)   Which voltmeter will show the smallest reading?

....

Parallel Circuits

Q1 Tick to show whether these statements about parallel circuits are **true** or **false**.

	True	False

a) The total current is the sum of the current through each component. ☐ ☐

b) Each component has the same potential difference across it. ☐ ☐

c) The current is the same everywhere in the circuit. ☐ ☐

d) Components can be switched on and off separately. ☐ ☐

Q2 The diagrams show currents at junctions in two parallel circuits.

Write in the **missing** values.

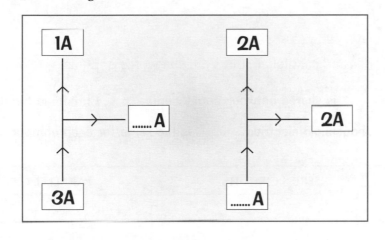

Hint: look at the arrows to see where the current is being split.

Q3 Find the **missing values** in this parallel circuit.

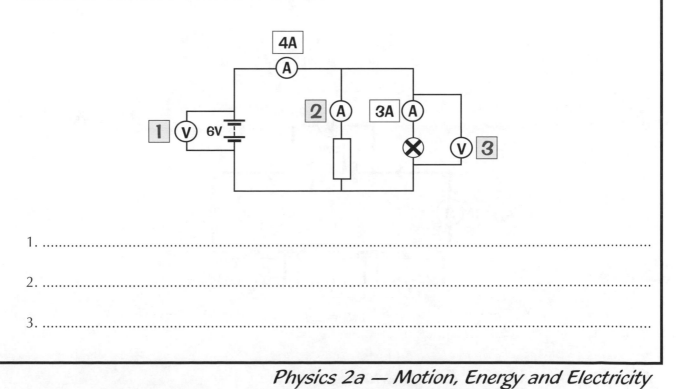

1. ....

2. ....

3. ....

Series and Parallel Circuits — Examples

Q1   A set of **Christmas tree lights** is designed to work on mains p.d. (230 V). It has **12 V** bulbs.
Complete the paragraph below by choosing either **series** or **parallel** in each highlighted pair.

> You can tell that the Christmas tree lights are wired in **series / parallel**
> because the p.d. across the individual bulbs is less that the mains p.d.
> supply. If they were wired in **series / parallel**, then each bulb would
> get the full p.d. of 230 V. It might be better to wire the Christmas tree
> lights in **series / parallel** because then if one were to fail, the others
> would stay on. However, this would require an adaptor.

Q2   **Complete** this table for series and parallel circuits using the words or phrases below.

separately to supply   is shared between components   Christmas tree lights

end to end   household electrics   is the same for each component

Some answers can be used more than once.

	SERIES CIRCUITS	PARALLEL CIRCUITS
Components connected		
Current		
Voltage		
Example of use		

Q3   Fill in the **four** missing values on this **series** circuit:

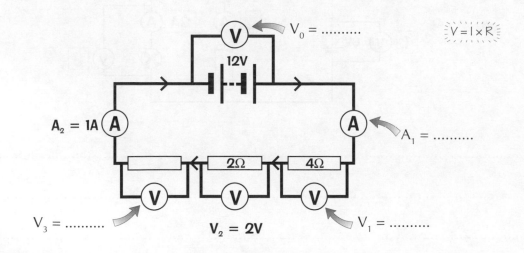

$V = I \times R$

$V_0 = \ldots\ldots\ldots$

$A_2 = 1A$ $A_1 = \ldots\ldots\ldots$

$12V$ 2Ω 4Ω

$V_3 = \ldots\ldots\ldots$ $V_2 = 2V$ $V_1 = \ldots\ldots\ldots$

Physics 2a — Motion, Energy and Electricity

Mixed Questions — Physics 2a

Q1 Mr Alonso drives his car at a constant speed for **1500 m**. The engine produces a force of **300 N**.

a) How much work does the engine do? Circle the correct answer.

300 N ➡

0.2 J   500 J   500 000 J   450 000 J   45 J

$w = F \times d$

b) Mr. Alonso then accelerates. His speed increases by **20 m/s** over **6.2 s**. Calculate his **acceleration**.

....

....

$a = \dfrac{change\ in\ velocity}{time}$

c) As it's a hot day, Mr. Alonso winds down his windows.
Suggest how this will alter the **top speed** of the car.

Hint: it makes the car less aerodynamic.

....

d) Explain (in terms of forces) how wearing a seat belt will keep Mr. Alonso safer in a crash.

....

....

Q2 Jack and Jill go up a hill to go on a roller coaster. With them in it, the roller coaster carriage has a total mass of **1200 kg**.

a) What is the **weight** of the carriage? (g = 10 N/kg.)

$W = m \times g$

....

....

b) At the start of the ride the carriage rises up to its highest point of **34 m** above the ground and stops. Calculate its gain in gravitational potential energy.

$E_p = m \times g \times h$

....

....

c) The carriage then falls to a point level with its initial position. Give its **kinetic energy** at this point.

....

d) At the end of the ride, the carriage slows down, decelerating at **6.4 m/s²**.
What is the **size** of the **force** needed to produce this deceleration?

$F = m \times a$

....

....

Mixed Questions — Physics 2a

Q3 Norman loves trainspotting. As a special treat, he not only notes the train numbers but plots a **distance-time** graph for two of the trains.

Write the letters A-C on the correct places on the distance-time graph to show:

(A) Where train 2 is travelling faster than train 1.

(B) Where train 2 is stationary.

(C) Where train 1 is decelerating.

Q4 Cherie and Tony rob a bank. They escape in a getaway car with a total mass of **2100 kg** and travel at a constant speed of **25 m/s** along a straight, level road.

a) Is there a resultant force on the car? Explain your answer.

....

....

b) Calculate the momentum of the car. $p = m \times v$

....

c) A police car swings into the middle of the road and stops ahead of Cherie's car. Cherie slams on the brakes. The car comes to a halt **5.0 s** after she hits the brakes.

   i) Write down **two** factors that could affect Cherie's thinking distance.

   1. ....

   2. ....

   ii) Calculate the **deceleration** of Cherie's car. $a = \dfrac{v - u}{t}$

   ....

   ....

Top Tips: These mixed questions are like a good quality pick 'n' mix — there's a bit of everything in there: velocity, force, work, momentum, mass... And that's just what the exam will be like.

Physics 2a — Motion, Energy and Electricity

Mixed Questions — Physics 2a

Q5 The diagram shows a circuit in which three resistors are connected in **series**.

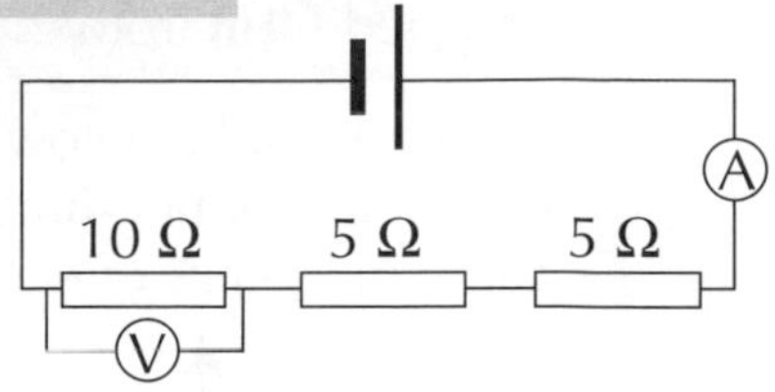

a) Calculate the total resistance of the three resistors.

....

b) If the ammeter shown reads 0.4 A, find:

$V = I \times R$

i) the reading on the voltmeter shown.

....

....

ii) the potential difference of the power supply.

....

....

Q6 Ian is investigating the way the current through a **resistor** changes with the potential difference across it.

a) In the box, sketch the circuit that Ian should use. It should include the resistor he's testing, a cell, a variable resistor, an ammeter and a voltmeter.

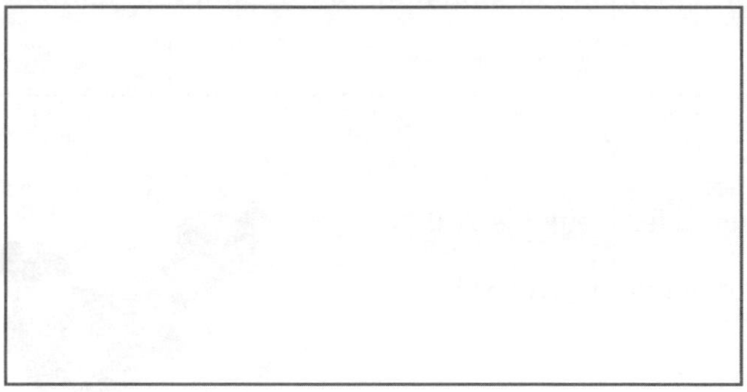

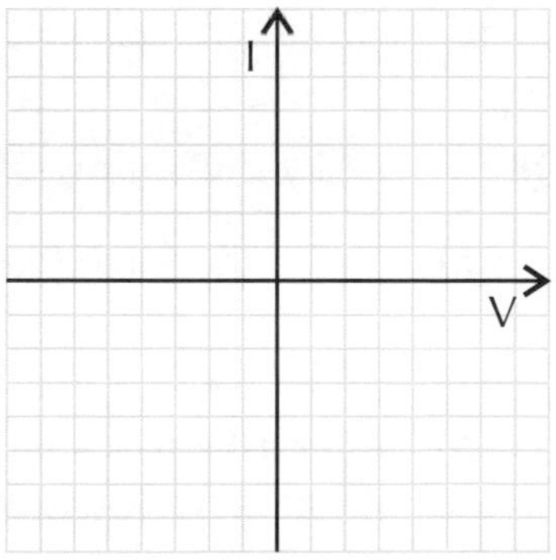

b) Sketch on the axes the graph that you would expect him to obtain.

c) Ian's car has a **thermostat** to regulate temperature in the engine.
Name the **type** of resistor used in a thermostat and briefly **describe** how this type of resistor works.

....

....

d) The diagram shows an oscilloscope trace from the mains electricity supply on the island where Ian lives. The **gain** dial was set to 50 V per division.

Calculate the **peak potential difference** of Ian's electricity supply.

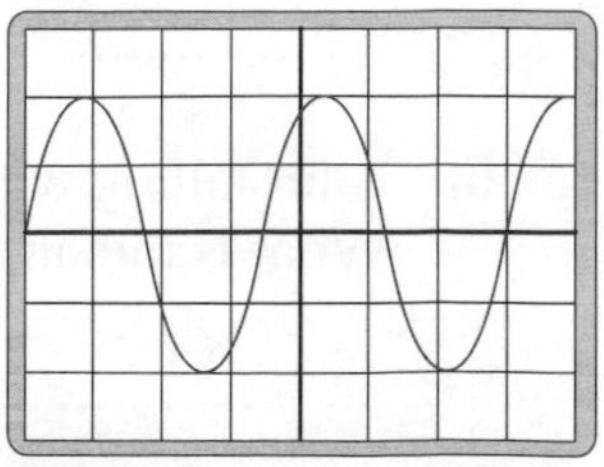

....

....

Mixed Questions — Physics 2a

Q7 In the film 'Crouching Sparrow, Hidden Beaver', a **95 kg** dummy is dropped **60 m** from the top of a building. (Assume that g = 10 m/s².)

a) The two graphs below show the motion of the dummy as it falls. One is a **distance-time graph**, and the other is a **velocity-time graph**. **Label** the **y-axis** of each graph.

time

time

b) The take doesn't go to plan so the dummy is lifted back to the top of the building using a motor.

i) How much **work** is done on the dummy to get it to the top of the building?

....

....

ii) It takes **7.5 s** for the motor to lift the dummy to the top of the building. Calculate the **useful power output** of the motor.

....

....

Q8 A sky-diver jumps out of an aeroplane. Her weight is **700 N**.

a) Name the force that causes her to accelerate downwards.

....

b) After **10 s** she is falling at a steady speed of **60 m/s**. What is the force of air resistance acting on her? Circle the correct answer.

| 700 N | 500 N | 600 N |

c) She now opens her parachute, which increases the air resistance to **2000 N**. Explain what effect this has on her downwards velocity.

....

....

d) After falling with her parachute open for 5 s, the sky-diver is travelling at a steady speed. What is the air resistance force now?

....

Mains Electricity

Q1   Choose from the words below to fill in the gaps.

hertz	alternating	volts	direct

In the United Kingdom the mains electrical supply is about 230 ....

The supply is .... current which means that the direction of the

current is constantly changing. The supply has a frequency of 50 cycles per second

(50 ....). Cells and batteries supply .... current

— the current always passes in the same direction.

Q2   The diagram shows three traces on the same oscilloscope screen.
The settings are the same in each case.

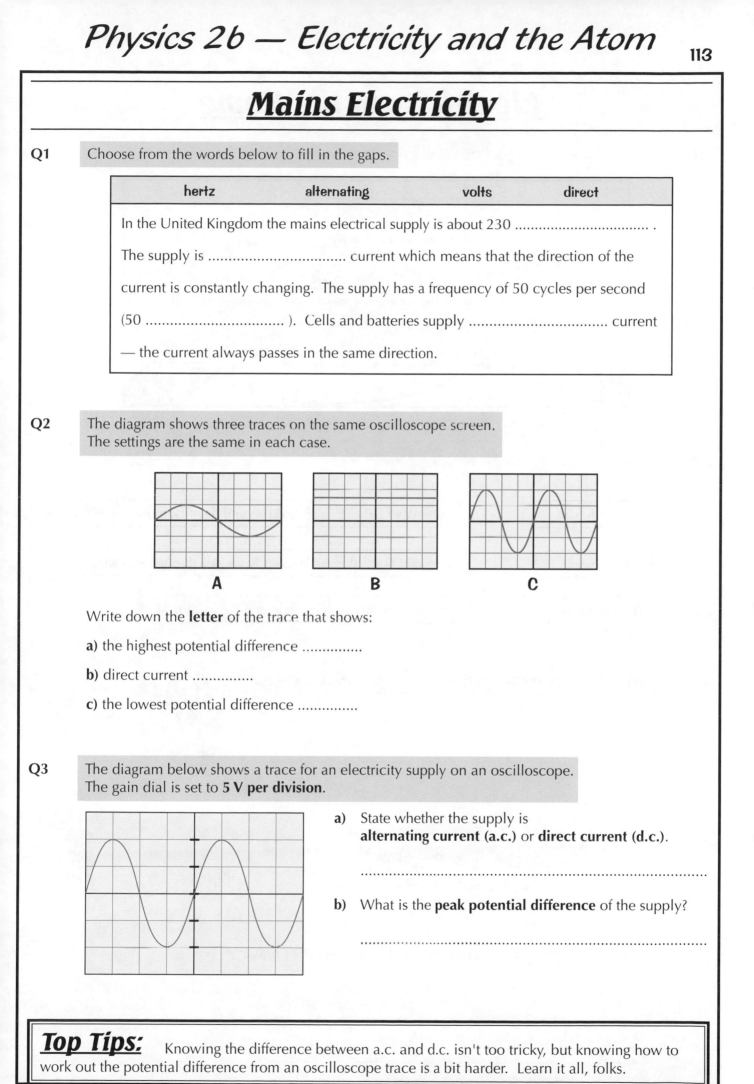

| **A** | **B** | **C** |

Write down the **letter** of the trace that shows:

a) the highest potential difference ....

b) direct current ....

c) the lowest potential difference ....

Q3   The diagram below shows a trace for an electricity supply on an oscilloscope.
The gain dial is set to **5 V per division**.

a)   State whether the supply is
alternating current (a.c.) or **direct current (d.c.)**.

....

b)   What is the **peak potential difference** of the supply?

....

Top Tips: Knowing the difference between a.c. and d.c. isn't too tricky, but knowing how to work out the potential difference from an oscilloscope trace is a bit harder. Learn it all, folks.

Electricity in the Home

Q1   Look at this picture of a kitchen. Put a **ring** round everything that is **unsafe**.

Q2   Draw lines to complete the sentences below.

| The earth wire... | ...alternates between high positive and negative potential difference. |

| The live wire... | ...stays at 0 V. Current usually flows out through this wire. |

| The neutral wire... | ...is there to protect the wiring and for safety. |

Q3   This plug is **incorrectly** wired. Write down the **three** mistakes.

= Neutral
= Live
= Earth

1. ....

2. ....

3. ....

Q4   Answer the following questions about **plugs**:

a)   Why is the body of a plug made of rubber or plastic?

   ....

b)   Explain why some parts of a plug are made from copper or brass.

   ....

c)   What material is the cable insulation made from, and why?

   ....

Fuses and Earthing

Q1 Fill in the gaps using the words from the box.

| safety | shocks | earthing | connected |

The main .... features of electric wiring in the home are

.... and fuses. These reduce the risk of fires and electric

.... It is important to make sure you use a correctly

rated fuse and have all the wires .... properly.

Q2 Many household appliances are fitted with a fuse for safety.

a) Put these events in the correct order to describe what happens
when a fault occurs in an earthed kettle. Label the events from 1 to 4.

☐ This breaks the circuit through the live wire so you don't get a shock from the case.

☐ The surge in current melts the fuse if it is bigger than the fuse rating.

☐ A big current flows out through the earth wire.

☐ A fault allows the live wire to touch the metal case.

b) Fuses have to be replaced once they've melted.
Name a safety feature that you can use instead of a fuse that would **not** need to be replaced.

....

Q3 Some circuits are protected by Residual Current Circuit
Breakers (RCCBs). Tick the boxes to show whether the
following statements about RCCBs are **true** or **false**.

	True	False
a) RCCBs break a circuit when they detect a surge in current.	☐	☐
b) They break the circuit by melting a wire.	☐	☐
c) Unlike fuses, they can easily be reset.	☐	☐
d) They operate much faster than fuses.	☐	☐
e) A big change in current is needed for an RCCB to break a circuit.	☐	☐

Fuses and Earthing

Q4 A '**double insulated**' hair dryer uses a current of 1.8 A.

a) Andrea has fuses rated 0.25 A, 2 A and 8 A.
    Which fuse should she fit in the plug for the hair dryer? ....

b) Why does the hair dryer **not** need an **earth wire**?

    ....

c) What type of electrical cable will the hair dryer have? Circle the correct answer.

    two-core cable   **three-core cable**

d) Andrea notices the electrical supply cable for her heater is much thicker than for her
    hair dryer. Explain how **cable thickness** and **fuse ratings** of appliances are **linked**.

    ....

    ....

Q5 Lucy is comparing **three lamps**. She connects each lamp in a circuit
    and measures the **current**. Her results are shown in the table below.

$P = I \times V$

	Lamp A	Lamp B	Lamp C
Voltage (V)	12	3	230
Current (A)	2.5	4	0.1
Power (W)			

a) Complete the table by filling in the missing values.

b) Typical fuse ratings are 1, 2, 3, 5, 7, 10 or 13 A. What rating of fuse would each lamp need?

    A = ...,   B = ...,   C = ...

Q6 An electric heater is rated at **230 V, 1500 W**.

$I = P \div V$

a) Calculate the current it uses.

    ....

    ....

b) What rating of fuse should be used with this heater? Circle your choice.

    1 A   2 A   3 A   5 A   7 A   10 A   13 A

Top Tips: RCCBs are becoming more and more common, mainly because they are a lot **safer**
than fuses. Unfortunately, you still need to be able to work out appliance fuse ratings. Sorry chaps.

Energy and Power in Circuits

Q1 Fill in the gaps using the words in the box.

power	energy	more	heat	time

The energy transferred by an appliance depends on how long it's used for

and its .... The power of an appliance can be calculated

using the formula: power = ... ÷ ....

Whenever an electrical current flows through anything with an electrical resistance,

electrical energy is converted into .... energy. The less energy

wasted, e.g. as heat by an appliance, the .... efficient it is.

Q2 Raj is comparing **three** different types of light bulb. Below is a summary of his findings.

	Compact Fluorescent Lamp (CFL)	Light-emitting diode (LED) bulb	Filament bulb
Energy efficiency	~10%	~75%	~2%
Cost	£3.50	£25	50p

a) Suggest **one** reason why the filament bulb has a low efficiency.

....

b) Suggest **one** reason why Raj might choose to buy the **LED** bulb rather than the other two types.

....

c) Suggest **one** reason why Raj might choose to buy the **filament** bulb rather than the other two types.

....

Q3 Calculate the **power rating** of the following electric appliances.

Remember to put time in seconds. $P = E \div t$

a) A lamp that transfers 1000 J in 10 seconds: ....

.... W

b) A motor that transfers 60 000 J in 2 minutes: ....

.... W

c) A heater that transfers 2000 J in 25 seconds: ....

.... W

Atomic Structure

Q1 Complete the following sentences using the words in the box below.

| protons | ions | zero | positive | electrons |

a) Neutral atoms have a .... charge.

b) Charged atoms are called ....

c) A neutral atom has the same number of .... and ....

d) If an electron is removed from a neutral atom, the atom has a .... charge.

Q2 **Complete** this table.

Particle	Mass	Charge
Proton	1	
	1	0
Electron		−1

Q3 In the early 1900s, **Rutherford** and **Marsden** performed experiments that led them to the **nuclear model** of the atom.

a) Circle the correct words in each pair to complete the description of Rutherford and Marsden's experiment.

Rutherford and Marsden wanted to test the **plum / apple** pudding model, which suggested that atoms were spheres of **negative / positive** charge with electrons stuck in them. They fired **beta / alpha** particles at a **thin / thick** gold foil, and expected the particles to be slightly deflected by the gold atoms. However, they saw that most of the particles went straight through the gold foil. This showed that most of the volume of the atom was just **neutrons / empty space**.

b) In their experiment, Rutherford and Marsden sometimes saw one of the fired particles coming **straight back at them**. Explain what this showed about the **structure of the atom**.

....

....

....

Atoms and Radiation

Q1 Tick the boxes to show whether these sentences are **true** or **false**.

True False

a) The total number of neutrons in an atom is called the atomic number. ☐ ☐

b) The total number of protons and neutrons in an atom is called the mass number. ☐ ☐

c) Atoms of the same element with the same number of neutrons are called isotopes. ☐ ☐

d) Radioactive decay speeds up at higher temperatures. ☐ ☐

e) Radioactive decay is a random process — you can't predict when it will happen. ☐ ☐

Q2 **Radiation doses** can be measured in **millisieverts (mSv)**.

a) While you are reading this you are receiving a radiation dose of about 2 mSv/year.

i) What is causing this?

....

ii) Suggest **two** sources that might contribute to this radiation.

1. ....

2. ....

b) The people pictured below are all likely be exposed to more radiation than average.
For each person, suggest why they have a higher than average radiation dose.

Pilot

....

....

Miner

....

....

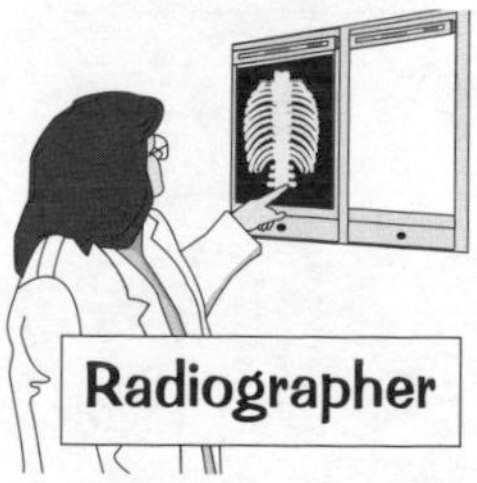

Radiographer

....

....

Ionising Radiation

Q1 Match up each type of radiation with its description.

Alpha particle   2 neutrons and 2 protons — the same as a helium nucleus.

Beta particle   A type of electromagnetic wave.

Gamma radiation   An electron.

Q2 Complete the table below by choosing the correct word from each column.

Radiation Type	Ionising power (weak/moderate/strong)	Penetrating power (low/moderate/high)	Range in air (short/long/very long)
alpha			
beta			
gamma			

Q3 What is the connection between the **ionising power** of radiation and its **penetrating power**? Circle the correct answer.

The lower the ionising power of radiation, the further it can penetrate into materials.

There is no connection between ionising power and penetrating power.

The higher the ionising power of radiation, the further it can penetrate into materials.

Q4 The diagram below shows the paths of the three types of ionising radiation in a **magnetic field**. Complete the diagram by correctly labelling the paths **alpha**, **beta** and **gamma**.

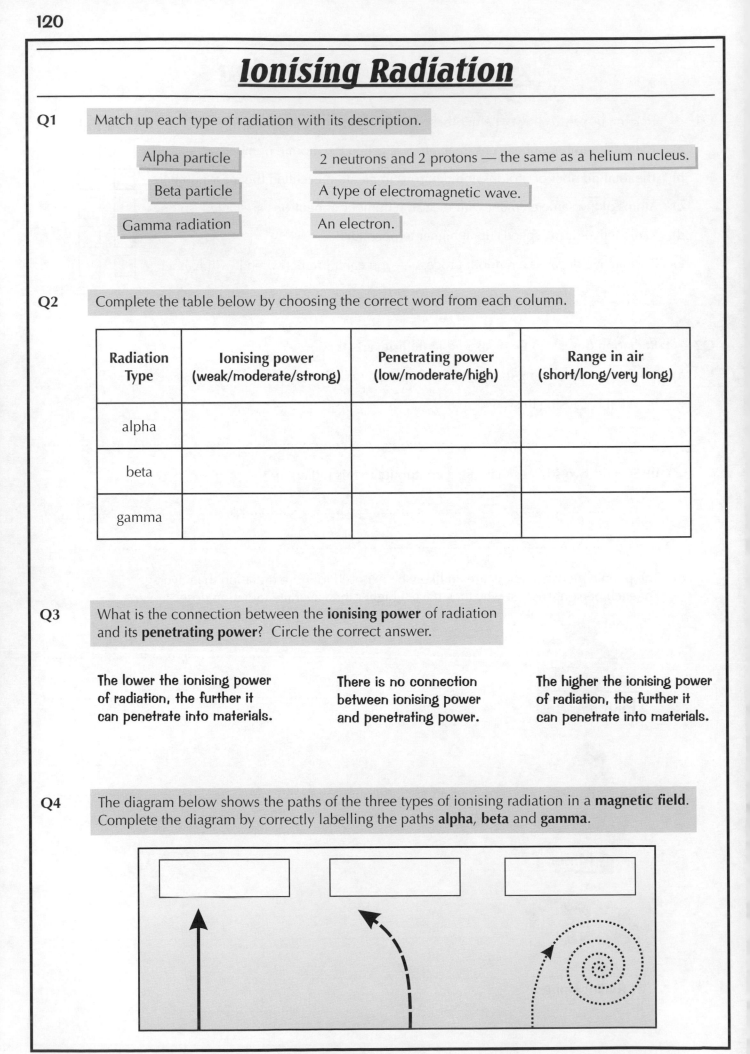

Physics 2b — Electricity and the Atom

Half-Life

Q1 Use the words in the box to complete the definition of half-life below.

halve	nuclei	time	activity	initial

Half-life is the average .... it takes for the number of

.... in a radioactive isotope sample to .... ,

or the time it takes for the .... of a sample to fall to half its

.... level.

Q2 A radioactive isotope has a half-life of **60 years**.
Which of these statements describes this isotope correctly? Tick **one** box only.

In 120 years there will be no radioactivity left in the material. ☐

In 30 years' time, only half the atoms will be radioactive. ☐

In 60 years' time, the activity will be half what it is now. ☐

In 180 years there will be no radioactivity left in the material. ☐

Q3 The half-life of strontium-90 is **29 years**. A scientist measures
the activity of a sample of strontium to be 1200 Bq.
Calculate what you would expect the activity to be after 87 years.

87 years is 3 × 29 years,
so 3 half-lives.

....

....

....

....

Q4 The activity of a radioactive sample is **1440 Bq**. 5 hours later
it has fallen to **45 Bq**. Calculate the half-life of this material.

....

....

....

Physics 2b — Electricity and the Atom

Uses of Radiation

Q1 The following sentences explain how a smoke detector works, but they are in the wrong order.

Put them in order by labelling them 1 (first) to 5 (last).

[ ] The circuit is broken so no current flows.

[1] The radioactive source emits alpha particles.

[ ] The alpha particles cause ionisation, and the ions form a current.

[ ] The alarm sounds.

[ ] A fire starts and smoke particles absorb the alpha radiation.

Q2 The table on the right shows the properties of three radioactive isotopes.

Radioactive isotope	Half-life	Type of emission
technetium-99	6 hours	beta/gamma
phosphorus-32	14 days	beta
cobalt-60	5 years	beta/gamma

a) Draw a circle around the isotope that would be most suitable for use as a medical tracer.

b) Give a reason for your answer to part **a)**.

....

Q3 The diagram shows how radiation can be used to sterilise surgical instruments.

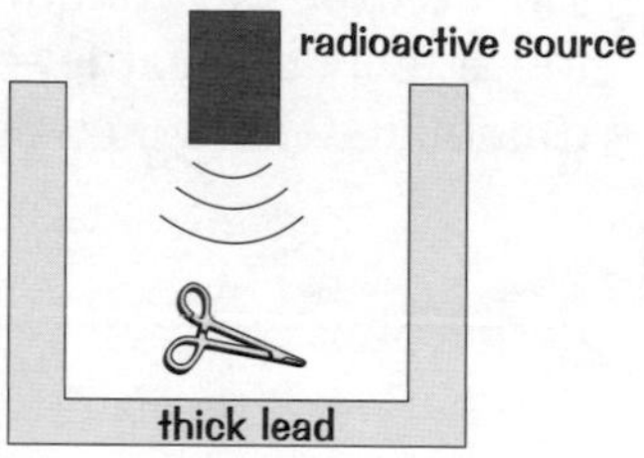

a) What kind of radioactive source (alpha, beta or gamma) is used to sterilise surgical instruments?

....

radioactive source

thick lead

b) Explain why the source used should have a long half-life.

....

....

c) Explain why thick lead is used to surround the surgical instruments whilst they're being sterilised.

....

HINT: Thick lead will stop alpha, beta and gamma radiation.

....

Top Tips: As well as being able to say which radioactive source is the best to use for a particular job, you've also got to be able to say why it's the best. You've got to think about stuff like the type of radiation it emits and what the half-life of the source is. Lots to think about folks.

Radioactivity Safety

Q1   The three different types of radiation can all be dangerous.

a) Which **two** types of radiation can pass through the human body?
Circle the correct answers.

alpha   beta   gamma

b) Which type of radiation is usually most dangerous if it's **inside** the body?

....

c) Complete the paragraph below on the dangers of radiation by circling the correct word in each pair.

> If radiation enters a living cell it can **bond / collide** with molecules such as DNA
>
> and cause **electrolysis / ionisation**. This can cause the cells to mutate and
>
> **divide / self-destruct** uncontrollably — this is cancer. **Higher / Lower** doses of
>
> radiation can damage the molecules within cells so much that the cell dies.
>
> This is called **electromagnetic / radiation** sickness, and it can make you feel very ill.

Q2   Two scientists are handling samples of radioactive material.

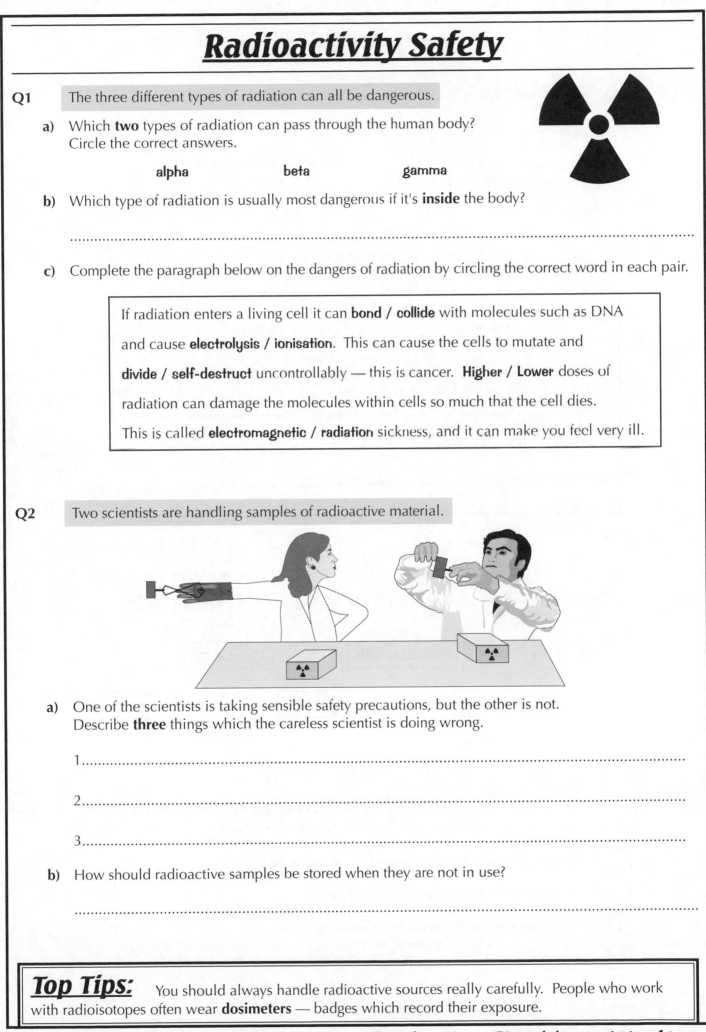

a) One of the scientists is taking sensible safety precautions, but the other is not.
Describe **three** things which the careless scientist is doing wrong.

1...

2...

3...

b) How should radioactive samples be stored when they are not in use?

....

Top Tips: You should always handle radioactive sources really carefully. People who work
with radioisotopes often wear **dosimeters** — badges which record their exposure.

Nuclear Fission

Q1   Circle the statement below that describes **nuclear fission**.

| Nuclear fission is the splitting of an atomic nucleus. | Nuclear fission is the joining of two atomic nuclei to form a larger one. |

Q2   Choose from the following words to complete the passage.

split	turbine	electricity	water
generator		energy	

Inside a nuclear reactor, atoms of the fuel .... and

release .... This is used to turn ....

into steam. The steam then turns a ...., which in turn

drives a ...., producing ....

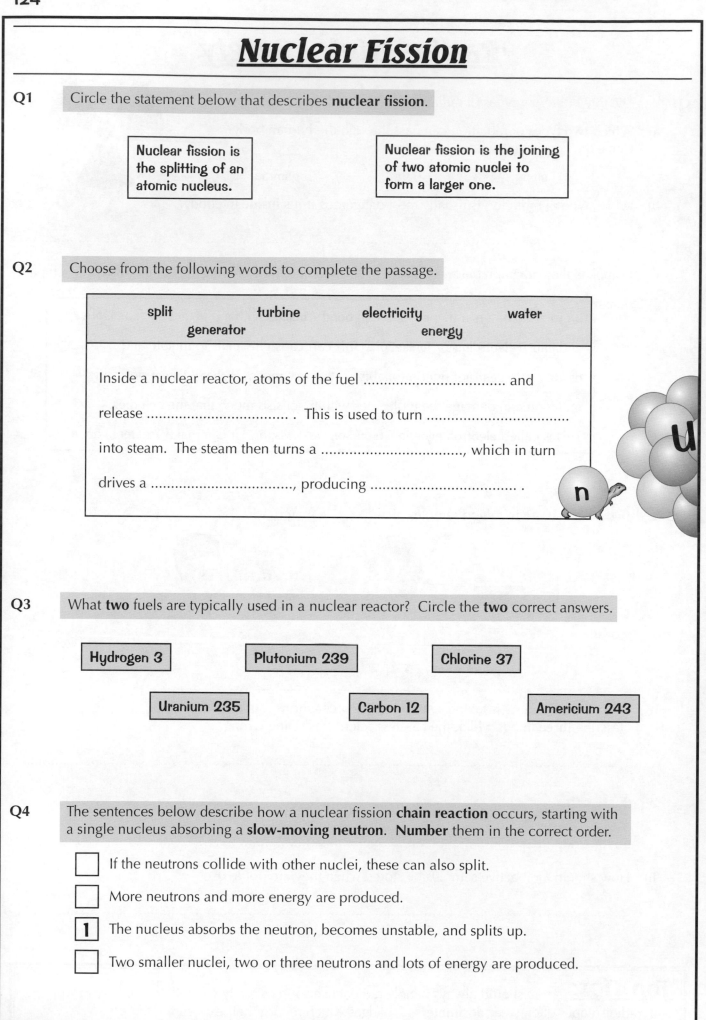

Q3   What **two** fuels are typically used in a nuclear reactor? Circle the **two** correct answers.

| Hydrogen 3 | Plutonium 239 | Chlorine 37 |

| Uranium 235 | Carbon 12 | Americium 243 |

Q4   The sentences below describe how a nuclear fission **chain reaction** occurs, starting with a single nucleus absorbing a **slow-moving neutron**. **Number** them in the correct order.

☐ If the neutrons collide with other nuclei, these can also split.

☐ More neutrons and more energy are produced.

1   The nucleus absorbs the neutron, becomes unstable, and splits up.

☐ Two smaller nuclei, two or three neutrons and lots of energy are produced.

Nuclear Fission and Fusion

Q1 For each of the statements below, tick the correct box to show whether they are describing a **fission** or a **fusion** reaction.

		Fission	Fusion
a)	A large nucleus is split up into two smaller nuclei.	☐	☐
b)	Two small nuclei are joined to form one larger one.	☐	☐
c)	Hydrogen is the main fuel for this type of reaction.	☐	☐
d)	Lots of radioactive waste is produced in this reaction.	☐	☐
e)	Extremely high temperatures are required for this to happen.	☐	☐

Q2 Nuclear power uses **nuclear fuel** and produces **radioactive waste**.

a) Circle the letter of the correct statement below that describes the **costs** involved in nuclear power.

> A — The overall cost of nuclear power is **low** because the fuel is cheap and the waste is easy to dispose of.

> B — The overall cost of nuclear power is **high** (even though the waste is easy to dispose of) because the fuel is very expensive.

> C — The overall cost of nuclear power is **high** (even though the fuel is quite cheap) because the waste is expensive to dispose of safely.

b) Other than radioactive waste, name **one risk** associated with nuclear power stations.

....

Q3 Give two good points and two bad points about **fusion reactors**.

Good points

1. ....

2. ....

Bad points

1. ....

2. ....

Physics 2b — Electricity and the Atom

The Life Cycle of Stars

Q1 The statements below describe what happens when a star about the size of the Sun starts to run out of fuel. Put the numbers 1-6 in the boxes to show the correct order.

| 1 | The star begins to run out of hydrogen and starts making heavier elements from the fusion of helium. |

One has already been done for you.

☐ The Red Giant becomes unstable.

☐ It ejects its outer layer of dust and gas.

☐ It cools and fades down to a Black Dwarf, before disappearing.

☐ The star then shrinks down to a White Dwarf.

☐ The star swells into a Red Giant.

Q2 Stars are formed from clouds of dust and gas.

a) Explain **why** the material comes together.

....

b) Describe how **planets** can form around a star.

....

....

....

....

Q3 The early universe only contained the element **hydrogen**.

Think about how new elements are formed.

a) Explain why the universe now contains lots of different elements.

....

b) Stars form heavy elements such as iron during their stable phases.
Describe how elements **heavier** than iron are created and **ejected** into the universe.

....

....

Mixed Questions — Physics 2b

Q1   The table gives information about four different **radioactive isotopes**.

a) What is different about the **nucleus** of **cobalt-60** compared to that of 'normal' **cobalt-59**?

....

....

Source	Type of Radiation	Half-life
radon-222	alpha	3.8 days
technetium-99m	gamma	6 hours
americium-241	alpha	432 years
cobalt-60	beta and gamma	5.27 years

b) Which source in the table would be most suitable for each of the uses below?

        medical tracer   **smoke detector**   **detecting leaks in pipes**

....

c) Radiation can be used to treat cancer.

i) What type of radiation is used in this treatment? ....

ii) Suggest why it is important that the radiation is carefully directed at the cancer cells.

....

d) i) Jim measures the activity of a sample of americium-241 as **160 Bq**.
Calculate how long would it take for the activity to fall to **40 Bq**. Show your working.

....

....

ii) Give **one** precaution Jim should take while handling the radioactive sample.

....

Q2   Modern electrical appliances are carefully designed to prevent the user getting an electric shock.

a) Tom's washing machine develops a fault. Part of the live wire touches the metal case.
Explain how the earth wire and fuse work together to prevent Tom getting an electric shock.

....

....

b) Bob buys a new 'double insulated' television set.

i) Which wires are in the plug?   ....

ii) What is meant by 'double insulated'?

....

....

Physics 2b — Electricity and the Atom

Mixed Questions — Physics 2b

Q3 The diagram below shows a nuclear reactor.

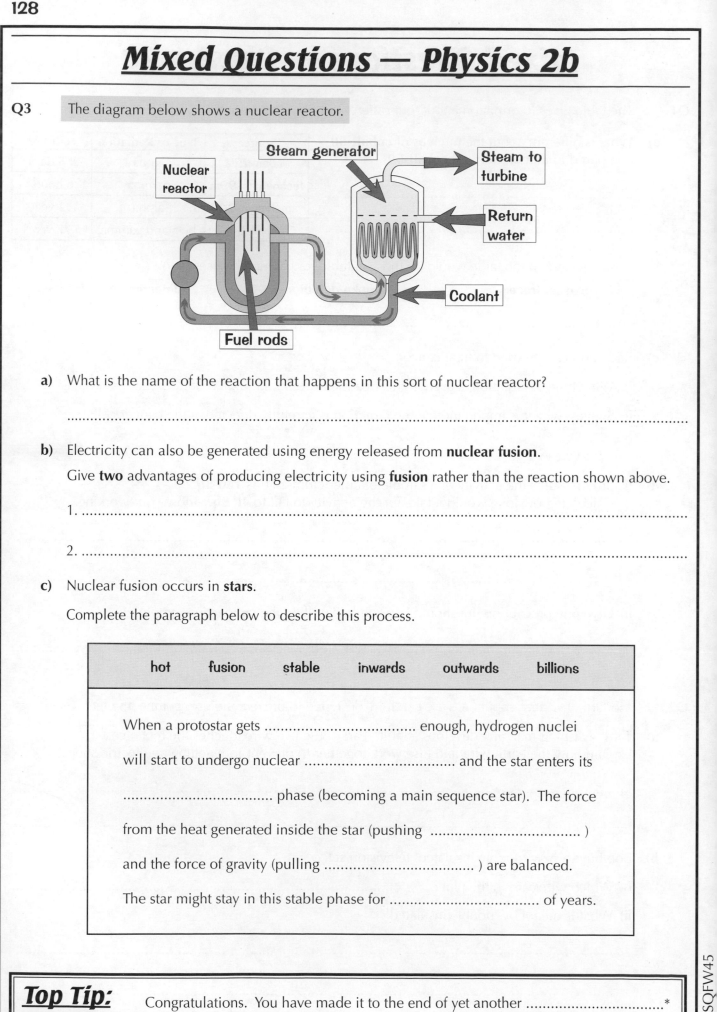

a) What is the name of the reaction that happens in this sort of nuclear reactor?

....

b) Electricity can also be generated using energy released from **nuclear fusion**.

Give **two** advantages of producing electricity using **fusion** rather than the reaction shown above.

1. ....

2. ....

c) Nuclear fusion occurs in **stars**.

Complete the paragraph below to describe this process.

hot	fusion	stable	inwards	outwards	billions

When a protostar gets .... enough, hydrogen nuclei

will start to undergo nuclear .... and the star enters its

.... phase (becoming a main sequence star). The force

from the heat generated inside the star (pushing ....)

and the force of gravity (pulling ....) are balanced.

The star might stay in this stable phase for .... of years.

Top Tip: Congratulations. You have made it to the end of yet another ....*
CGP workbook. May I suggest some sort of celebratory dance... Dum dada dum dada dum macarena...

Physics 2b — Electricity and the Atom   *insert appropriate word here